HANSSEN'S COMPLETE CIDER VINEGAR

Explains the many facets of cider vinegar, including its use in cooking and healing. With a selection of recipes and notes on the composition and manufacture of this 'miracle food'.

D0313611

HANSSEN'S COMPLETE CIDER VINEGAR

by

MAURICE HANSSEN
Member of the Royal Society of Health

THORSONS PUBLISHERS LIMITED
Wellingborough, Northamptonshire

First published 1974
Second Impression 1975
Third Impression 1976
Fourth Impression 1977
Fifth Impression 1978
Second Edition, revised
and reset, 1979

ISBN 0 7225 0576 0

Photoset by Specialised Offset Services Ltd, Liverpool
and printed and bound in Great Britain by
Hunt Barnard Printing Ltd, Aylesbury, Buckinghamshire

'Maurice Hanssen, in this comprehensive and well-researched book covers every aspect of cider vinegar from culinary to medicinal use.' – *The Vegetarian.*

'It is full of vital information and every mother should read it. It is, to my mind, the best money's worth to which you can treat yourself and your family.' – *Barbara Cartland in Here's Health.*

CONTENTS

FOREWORD

The merits of cider vinegar have been celebrated in print before now, but never — I suspect — accompanied by the thorough research and scientific accuracy displayed by Maurice Hanssen. To have done this in a reasonably light-hearted way adds to the readability.

Commencing with a detailed description of manufacturing processes from the time of autumn apple-picking, Maurice Hanssen continues with valuable information on the best way to take cider vinegar therapeutically and gives a detailed breakdown of the minerals, organic matter and acetic acid found in this most intriguing substance.

Cider vinegar is probably best known for its slimming properties, and Maurice Hanssen quotes chapter and verse for its success in this direction, and this quality alone should create very great interest. A natural substance really does inspire confidence. But cider vinegar has also been used with notable success in the treatment of arthritis and rheumatism, insomnia, asthma, and heart conditions. These — and other disorders — are all dealt with, and clear instructions for the internal and external application of cider vinegar are provided.

Like Maurice Hanssen, I believe in the importance of eating whole foods uncontaminated by chemical additives. Therefore I am delighted to find that his penultimate section is entitled 'Cider vinegar in the kitchen', and that it contains a host of appetizing recipes for salad dressings, sauces, chutneys, savoury dishes and drinks – all depending on the 'magic' ingredient of cider vinegar for their excellence. Dr Johnson declared, 'He who does not mind his stomach will not mind much else', and I for one cannot imagine a better introduction to cider vinegar than that supplied in the culinary information you will find in this section.

That cider vinegar has a role to play in animal husbandry, I find very reassuring. We live in a world where animals are too often subjected to 'feed' and 'medication' (though not in this country), under conditions which fill one with disquiet. Perhaps it is time that natural materials should be more widespread.

Burntwood
House of Lords
Past Chairman, National Association
for Health
Formerly Deputy Minister of Health
in Her Majesty's Government

PREFACE
TO NEW EDITION

The last five years have seen a rapid increase in the use of cider vinegar. Many readers have written to me, confirming by their own experiences, the effectiveness of cider vinegar as a treatment in those many disorders which can benefit from the subtle blend of natural substances, the actions of which we still do not begin to comprehend.

There have been exciting new developments in the use of cider vinegar in the supplementation of animal feeds. The remarkable story of the cow, Eva, a cow who has now produced 140 tons of milk and is still going strong at sixteen years of age. Racehorses, too, have improved their condition and performance.

It is such successes as these with animals that convince me more than anything else, that cider vinegar is not just another old wive's tale but that it really does contain substances of value, if not to all, then to very many people and animals.

There have been big changes in the methods of manufacture and there is now available, for the first time, a genuine organically grown cider vinegar of excellent quality.

For the gourmet, cider vinegar remains the condiment *par excellence*, and no kitchen cupboard is complete without a bottle or two.

INTRODUCTION

A miracle food? Can there be such a thing – a panacea for many ills, a safe aid to slimming, wonderful in the kitchen, good for animals – and not expensive?

My own researches into the effects of cider vinegar began in 1956 when I was frankly sceptical of apparently wild and baseless claims. Previously my work had been with the development of pharmaceuticals. I was aware of the controlled experiments and weight of evidence to be produced before claims could be made. Nonetheless, friends and friends of friends kept coming forward with reports of relief from long-standing complaints, with fatness going down on diets somehow suddenly simpler to obey. Complexions improved, the basic functions became once more normal. Perhaps, then that is the key idea behind cider vinegar therapy – to make normal.

Cider vinegar will not work in every way for every person, there are those who it simply upsets, those who find no effect at all – and those who find opening for them a wonderful new chapter in a life which had begun to fail in quality.

Orthodox medicine has in recent years greatly increased our chances of attaining middle age and nowhere would I wish my reader to avoid seeking medical advice when this is needed. But cider vinegar is not a drug, it is not normally antagonistic to other treatments. It is suitable for diabetics, for people on low salt diets, little children, old people and even animals.

Where the orthodox ideas have failed is in substantially increasing the life expectancy of the middle-aged. We have only a 5 year improvement for men and 8 years for women aged 45, in the past century. I believe that a main cause of this is poor nutrition. Whilst three-quarters of the world suffers from malnutrition most of the rest suffer in a different way; from over-nutrition. Cider vinegar appears to provide certain minerals and other elements needed by a very large number of almost healthy individuals.

My purpose in writing this book is to pass on to you the long and critical experience I have had in using and recommending cider vinegar. To tell you of the reasons why more than 1,000 regular users find real benefit. I shall let you come with me in your imagination around the main places where it is produced in Britain so that you know exactly what real cider vinegar is and the questions to ask when offered a new make. You will be able to try cider vinegar for culinary use with the wonderful and practical recipes I have collected. You will be guided in your efforts to become slim and I shall even provide a beauty secret or two.

None of this would have been possible without two great pioneers in the use of cider vinegar – Cyril Scott, the eminent composer, mystic and practical healer who first introduced it to Britain in 1948 with a book called *Cider Vinegar* and Dr D.C. Jarvis who followed up his articles in the American magazine *The Medical World* with his two revealing books on the effectiveness of Vermont country medicine, *Folk Medicine* and *Arthritis and Folk*

Medicine. Dr Jarvis published his first book in 1960. Since then many more case histories have been reported and more uses discovered. Many hundreds of friends and correspondents have asked me to recommend a comprehensive and up-to-date survey of cider vinegar. It is for them that I write this book and also in the hope that countless more will be happier and healthier as a result.

CHAPTER ONE

HOW CIDER VINEGAR IS MADE

In time past, cider vinegar was cider that had 'gone wrong'. Today, such is the need for a reliable and effective product that there is no such easy way out for the producers. The three main brands, Applefords, Martlet and Whiteways, use a basically similar method with certain differences which I shall point out where appropriate. An exception is Aspall who are employing a revolutionary new system of making cider vinegar from cider. All these firms have been most helpful in the compilation of this chapter and, indeed, in revealing helpful details from their private files regarding special uses and effects.

The apples arrive in September and October. Lorries full of freshly picked, specially grown, apples in the peak of condition. At Applefords the main crop is from the shiny Somerset cider apple, so full of minerals and acidity that it is not really possible to eat, even cooked with raw sugar! Martlet specialize in the firm fruity Bramley from the Kent and Sussex orchards, full of flavour and fragrance. Whiteways use Devon apples, not perhaps so tart as those from Somerset, but producing an excellent cider. Aspall have over eighty acres of organically maintained orchards in Suffolk.

Until recently, after the whole apples had been

coarsely chopped, they would be fed into hydraulic presses which sent volumes of delectable fresh apple juice coursing into cool, underground vats. The once-pressed pulp was then transferred to another press and squeezed until the apples became almost dry. Today, the apples go through an enormous rotary and continuous press which extracts the juice even more surely than the presses of old. When the apple remains reach the end, all the juice has gone and what is left is sent to be converted into organic compost or apple pectin. This is the setting agent used to provide the right consistency in good jams and conserves. I have always found it good to know that the apple is so completely used for our health, nutrition and good eating.

The apple juice goes then into large vats, usually, of Russian oak because only those huge trees provide perfect staves of sufficient length and quality. A culture of yeast begins the fermentation which completely changes all the sugar in the apple juice into alcohol. The time this takes depends upon the temperature and on certain other factors, but is about 3-4 weeks. After this, cider needs to mature for about six months – much longer than the four or five weeks needed for beer in a brewery – and then we are ready to make the vinegar.

The final process is called acetification. The traditional process, which is now superseded, was to acetify in huge 20,000 gallon vats made of Columbian pine or New Zealand Kauri pine although there was no reason why the stainless steel or fibre glass vats or glass lined steel vats which are replacing them should not be just as good. The vat had a web of lathes upon which sterilized four-feet layers of birch twigs were put until the vat contained some two tons of twigs. These were steamed for forty-eight hours prior to use. the twigs were then soaked in alcohol from cider mixed with some vinegar that was from a freshly working vat. This allowed the micro-organism, a bacterium called *Acetobacter* to become well established on the birch twigs.

The cider was then added in 5,000 gallon batches and circulated through the acetifier for two or three weeks. This allowed plenty of oxygen to be present which is necessary for the *Acetobacter* to convert entirely the alcohol into acetic acid. When this process had been completed the vinegar was lightly filtered into storage vats, of aged oak, where it developed flavour and any sediment was thrown.

Today, the invention of the *'Fring's Acetator'* has speeded up the changing of alcohol into acetic acid without any loss of quality. In fact, there is every chance that quality is increased in modern cider vinegars because the enclosed Fring's process very much reduces the loss of the vital ingredients by evaporation, which often occurred in the traditional method.

In the *Fring's Acetator* the *Acetobacter* grows in a suspension of fine air bubbles and fermenting liquid. This causes a very even distribution of the *Acetobacter* through the cider and the change, under carefully controlled conditions, takes only a few days. Half the tank is usually ready to use whilst the other half is being transformed, so the result is a more or less continuous supply of high quality cider vinegar. Both processes produce an acetic acid content which depends on the efficiency of the equipment but is usually around 7 per cent. This is far too strong for normal use so it is then diluted to about 4.8 per cent before being bottled. (See analyses for further information.)

The production at Martlet has increased so much over the past years that they have now installed a very advanced *Fring's Acetator* called the *'Continuo'*. As the name implies, this produces a continual supply of cider vinegar and it is much more efficient to use than the old batch process. The *'Continuo'* is especially suitable for lower strengths of vinegar, and is thus especially valuable in preserving the high mineral content that we look for in our best products.

Aspall use the *'Greenshields'* process for the continuous production of their vinegar, and Rod Greenshields of the University of Aston, a distinguished expert in fermentation technology, with his engineer brother Michael, told me about their machines with great enthusiasm.

The *'Greenshields'* process was developed at the University of Aston in Birmingham by Francis Harmon Limited and is covered by a British patent. The apparatus is made of high-grade plastic and uses a tubular fermenter through which passes a stream of bubbles. There are no moving parts and the fermenting liquid passes through it continuously, allowing the *Acetobacter* to grow and produce the vinegar naturally and without forced agitation.

Aspall was the first company to introduce this plant for the production of cider vinegar which, like Fring's system, has high efficiency, reduces losses and also minimizes the loss of vital constituents of the cider vinegar. The *'Greenshields'* system has great flexibility because the *Acetobacter* can still be maintained in healthy condition even when the air is stopped. This process is ideally suitable for both the smallest cider vinegar producer and the larger manufacturer.

Once in the bottle, it is important that the vinegar does not oxydize or grow moulds. For this reason it is necessary to add a substance which deters the oxygen from affecting the vinegar. The usual substance is sulphur dioxide. This was first known to have been used some 2,000 years ago by the ancient Greeks who burnt sulphur in the top of barrels of wine before sealing them down. The U.K. Food Laws state that the maximum allowable content of sulphur dioxide in cider vinegar is 70 parts per million, which is one of the lowest permitted figures for food products.

Whiteways cider vinegar is now made without any preservatives at all, as is Aspalls. It is to the credit of these manufacturers that they use such healthy methods of maintaining the quality of their products.

Martlet cider vinegar is sold in its natural, light straw-coloured state, as is that of Aspall and Whiteways. Applefords makes both a golden and a darker variety which is coloured with a little burnt sugar caramel to a pleasing rich brown.

For the technically minded, the change of the alcohol into vinegar (acetic acid) follows this chemical chain:

$$CH_3CH_2OH \xrightarrow{-2H} CH_3CHO \xrightarrow{(0)} CH_3COOH$$

ethyl alcohol   acetaldehyde   acetic acid

The greatest possible yield is 1.3 grams of acetic acid from 1.0 gram of alcohol and this is nearly reached in modern equipment.

The great mystery is why these changes to cider that transform it to cider vinegar also create such a remarkable aid to health for so many people.

CHAPTER TWO

CHOOSING THE RIGHT CIDER VINEGAR

As you will have read in the chapter on how cider vinegar is made, in simple terms cider vinegar is just vinegar made from cider. The shopper has many makes to choose from. Which is best for him?

In Britain there are four main producers, Applefords, Martlet, Whiteways and Aspall. These are all makers of different cider vinegars of the very highest quality. The main producers all also do some bottling for other firms. Quite soon it will be necessary to make it clear on the label if the contents are imported. The tests and results of this book were all made using British cider vinegars. Dr Jarvis has obtained good results with his American products.

I cannot speak for those made in other lands except to say that analyses of Swiss cider vinegar imported into Britain show a marked reduction in the mineral content. For example, the amount of potassium in the Swiss product is approximately half the British. Therefore beware of vinegars where the shopkeeper cannot tell you if they are British or from abroad. As I said, the only acceptable alternative supply appears to be American, at least until many more tests are carried out.

Whiteways call their vinegar 'cyder', whilst

Martlet and Appleford's call theirs 'cider'. Although Whiteways are probably Britain's oldest producer, they have been making it for more than 100 years, the 'cyder' spelling is not significant. In fact from the earliest times writers have been in two minds (or more) over the spelling. Neither is incorrect, as you will find if you examine the history of the name. There was a late Latin word *sicera*, which meant intoxicating liquor or strong drink. This was often used in the Bible of that time. In due course the word became altered, first to *sizra* and then to *sidra*.

Apples are a native fruit of Britain, in fact it is thought to be one of the only fruits to spread from East to West.

Some of the old names for varieties of cider apples charmingly remind us of an earlier era. Some of my favourites include *Avalon, Sweet Alford, Kingston Black, White Close Pippin, Yarlington Mill, Ponsford, Fair Maid of Devon, Cap of Liberty, Porter's Perfection* and, perhaps cheekily or perhaps because even in those days cider was thought of as helping people to slim – *Slack Ma Girdle*!

There may well have been cultivated orchards in Britain since Neolithic times for cider making. In the thirteenth-century the bailiff's account of the Earl of Devon's estate at Exminster showed a large production of cider. In 1724, Daniel Defoe, of *Robinson Crusoe* fame, wrote that 'Between Topsham and Axminster so much fruit grew and so much cider was made that sometimes they send to London between ten and twenty thousand hogshead of cider each year'. A hogshead is approximately 60 gallons (275 litres). No doubt cider making began on a large scale as a way of preserving the goodness of apples and, indeed, vitamin C, through the winter months.

Literature began to refer commonly to cider in the fourteenth century. Interesting references include the following:

1398 — Trevisa wrote, 'Honey cometh of floures, sidre of frute and ale of corne'.

1497 — Bishop Alcock wrote, 'Saynt John Baptyst wich ete neuer flesshe, dranke no wyne nor cydre'.

1626 — Francis Bacon wrote about sider; in 1663 Boyle talked of syder and perry.

1708 — J. Phillips wrote, 'My mill now grinds choice apples and the British vats o'erflow with generous cider'.

1767 — Hutchinson wrote, 'A barrel full of cyder'. In his *History of England* at about the same time, Macaulay recorded, 'Hogsheads of their best cyder'.

1875 — Jevons wrote, 'The farm labourer may partially receive payment in cider'.

So the different spellings change from age to age and run simultaneously together without there being a particular regional or other significance. You can therefore use, with a clear conscience, cyder *or* cider vinegar!

The cost has, considering the general way in which money has been devalued over the last 75 years, remained remarkably modest. In 1906, Whiteways listed apple vinegar in champagne bottles at a trade price of 7/6d (37½ new pence) a dozen. The larger sizes, which are by far the most economical if you use a lot, are perhaps 10-15 times as much today. When you remember that a goodish working wage was £50 a year in 1907, cider vinegar becomes one of today's bargains.

THE BASIC TREATMENT

The standard way in which I recommend the taking of cider vinegar is to mix two teaspoonsful in a tumbler of cold or warm water. Take one glassful first thing in the morning, one during or after lunch and one in the evening.

Different users find that different makes of cider vinegar work best for them so, if the first one you try does not seem to produce the hoped-for results, then try another. Some people with sensitive stomachs may find two teaspoonsful too much for them. In such cases, start with one teaspoonful until you are used to the effects.

Children under the age of about eight years also usually find the small dose sufficient. Infants can, of course, use less still but many babies and children really enjoy vinegar! A sweet tooth tends to be developed by the parents because they associate sweetness with reward. This is not to the advantage of a child's health – a 'vinegar tooth' is far better with a preference for savoury foods.

HONEY AND CIDER VINEGAR

Dr Jarvis recommends for many cases a mixture of honey and cider vinegar. The ideal seems to be equal volumes of the two ingredients. By weight this is equivalent to 42 per cent of cider vinegar and 58 per cent of honey.

This is very much an individual thing. Many who find cider vinegar either upsetting their stomach or not working well, find the mixture, which can be obtained in a prepared form, the perfect answer. If you mix your own, be sure to use an unblended pure honey. It does not matter if it is set or clear. Do *not* heat the mixture, as this is not good for certain constituents. The mixture is especially effective for hay fever and for asthma. My own view is that the honey helps the absorption, in certain cases, besides being itself valuable.

CHAPTER THREE

THE COMPOSITION OF CIDER VINEGAR

The active principles in cider vinegar come from the combination of minerals, organic matter and acetic acid in a naturally produced blend. There are certain to be fluctuations from time to time because of variations in the apple. All produce a sufficiently high potassium content to ensure the efficacy of the product. Different vinegars suit different persons depending upon the balance required.

The figures quoted are in grammes (g) per 100 millilitres (ml) or, where appropriate, in milligrammes (mg) or parts per million (p.p.m.).

For the general reader this information is not of much importance but as, so far as I can ascertain, it has not previously been published in book form, the analyses are included to make this survey as comprehensive as possible. Where I do not have specific information, this has been left out. This does not mean that the substance is actually absent.

Applefords — analysis per 100 mls.

Total solid matter	3.31 g
Acetic acid	4.75 g
Sugars (as invert)	0.45 g
Mineral ash	0.32 g
Tannins	0.015g
Calcium	8.2 mg
Phosphorus	4.85 mg

Sodium	7.0 mg
Potassium	100 mg
Riboflavin (vitamin B2)	trace
Nicotinic Acid	trace
Iron	0.05 p.p.m.
Copper	0.025 p.p.m.

Martlet – analysis per 100 mls.

Total solid matter	1.36 g
Acetic Acid	5.40 g
Sugars (as invert)	0.40
Mineral ash	0.24 g
Tannins	0.002 g
Protein	0.08 g
Calcium	7.1 mg
Phosphorus	6.5 mg
Sodium	12.0 mg
Potassium	103.0 mg
Iron	1.3 mg
Lead	nil
Arsenic	nil
Copper	0.54 p.p.m.
Zinc	0.10 p.p.m.
Riboflavin (vitamin B2)	trace
Nicotinic Acid	0.02 mg

Whiteways – analysis per 100 mls.

Total Solid matter	2.70 g
Acetic Acid	5.51 g
Sugars (as invert)	0.50 g
Sugar Free Dry Extract	2.19 g
Mineral Ash	0.22 g
Tannins	0.42 g
Protein	0.06 g
Calcium	4.8 mg

Phosphorus	4.7 mg
Sodium	3.24 mg
Potassium	85.3 mg
Iron	0.2 mg
Lead	nil
Arsenic	nil
Copper	0.01 mg
Zinc	0.05 mg
Riboflavin (vitamin B2)	trace
Nicotinic Acid	trace
Ascorbic Acid (vitamin C)	150 p.p.m.

Some Continental cider vinegars are made by using a very strong alcohol cider as the starting material, making the resulting acid content as high as thirteen or fourteen per cent, and then diluting the whole lot with water down to the normal acidity levels. This does, of course, mean that the mineral contents are reduced.

The analyses of these three main makes of vinegar are entirely satisfactory for our purposes. It all depends which suits you as to which you use.

Aspall cider vinegar is another excellent product of good analytical quality as well as being organically grown.

CHAPTER FOUR

CIDER VINEGAR FOR HEALTH

Describing the remarkable results of cider vinegar in a variety of complaints, one day, a friend said to me, in a scathing tone, 'Cider Vinegar seems to cure everything except corns!' It is true that the use is very wide in application. But, to draw a lesson from my friend's rebuke, I would say to you that corns do not usually trouble people with perfect shoes. In the same way, illness is minimized in a perfectly fit body.

Fitness comes from having sufficient exercise, enough sleep, a realistic and positive attitude of mind and *a well managed diet.* I believe that cider vinegar contains minute quantities of minerals which help to adjust our metabolism, or bodily processes, that are frequently missing when we eat.

That grand old pioneer of German natural medicine in the last century, Father Sebastian Kneipp, had the right attitude when he said that, if a person came to him with an open ulcer in the leg he would begin the treatment by looking at what his patient ate, then correct his diet because the ulcer is only the outward sign of an inward imbalance which must be corrected to achieve a real cure. We are often all too ready to rush to the medicine chest when we should be looking at our lifestyle as well. Cider vinegar has been called a panacea. Not because it has a strong drug-like action with unwelcome and often unsuspected side effects, but because cider vinegar makes the body normal.

Also for this reason cider vinegar cannot be guaranteed to work every time for everybody. But it *does* work, and work marvellously, for hundreds and thousands of men, women and children throughout the world.

Dr Jarvis carried out some experiments on cows to see if, as had been thought, it was the phosphorus in cider vinegar which was the vital and required element. It was not, and the final answer must await trials which will cost a great deal of money to carry out and which will not alter the fact which you can profit by straight away – that it really works for a very large number of people.

I mentioned earlier that over a thousand people had helped to establish some real and basic information by telling me why they used cider vinegar successfully. This work was done with Appleford's Cider Apple Vinegar. Martlet have carried out successful controlled trials using a mixture of honey and cider vinegar for the treatment of hay fever and of asthma. Martlet, Whiteways, Applefords and Aspall have each much experience in the veterinary uses. It is for me this last usage, for animals, that convinces me that the use of cider vinegar is not strange or unreasonable. I simply do not believe that animals can be fooled into health through cider vinegar. They recover because it works and, if it works for them, why should it not for us?

I will discuss the results of the survey and the recommended dosages under each category of complaint but, for the sake of interest, here are the various uses and the number of users in each main section:

General Health (Vigour, happiness, etc.)	426
General Qualities and Benefits	214
Slimming	184
Cooking	38
Rheumatism	39
Arthritis	39
'Flu, Colds, Catarrh, Sore Throat	16
Wrinkles	2
Blood Purification	2
Hay Fever	14
Toe and Finger Nails	4
Backache	4
Varicose Veins	4
Asthma	11
Skin Troubles	2
Insomnia	7
Digestive Disturbances	34
Cataract	1
Heart Troubles	17
Cramp	4
Shingles	5
High Blood-Pressure	12
	1,079

Remember, as you read the descriptions of the various complaints, that they are *all* based on actual and recent case histories supported by 'the experience of previous writers and users over very many years.' Also, I will take this opportunity of thanking Appleford's Martlet, Whiteway's and Aspall for the help they have given in the compilation of what is the first comprehensive book on cider vinegar therapy. But we must also thank them for making this remarkable food available. Other countries also have cider vinegars of great quality. Check with the analytical chapter if you are not in Britain and find a type to suit you and your body's needs.

SLIMMING

Life assurance companies have known for a long time from their carefully kept records that fatness and health do not often go together.

Fatness does not look very attractive, at least not to Western eyes, and more children are unable to adjust to a happy school relationship with their fellows because they are ungraceful and ungainly fatties.

Cider vinegar helps you to achieve a normal diet. It improves the functioning and adjustment of the body so that there is efficient use made of the food you eat and you become very satisfied and content with the right amount.

Before embarking on your slimming with cider vinegar be sure to examine your present diet to see that it is well balanced and healthy. Cider vinegar can do a lot for you, but it is better if you provide yourself with the right nutritious diet as well. Check yourself:

1. Do I eat wholemeal bread and flour products? There is now overwhelming evidence that some of the diseases of western civilization, especially those in the colon or lower part of the gut, are caused by not taking enough cereal fibre. Apart from the nutrients present in foods it is now

certain that the physical quality is also important to health. So the day when we can live on a diet of space-age pills may never arrive. Thank goodness for that!

2. Do I eat too much sugar? (The average intake of sugar in the U.K. is about 120 pounds (55 kilos) a year. That is for every man, woman and child. I know I don't have my share, so many must have far more. Sugar, apart from making you fat, helps cause tooth decay, affects the blood and may cause heart trouble in some people.)

3. Am I sure to eat some green vegetable and some fruit each day? (Fruit, especially citrus, provides vitamin C. Vegetables are best lightly cooked or steamed in the minimum of water. Use the stock for soups as it contains water soluble vitamins and minerals.)

4. Do I include protein in my daily diet? (Protein builds muscles and repairs the cells. It cannot be stored for long so is needed daily. Proteins come from nuts, soya beans, milk, eggs, cheese, fish and lean meat.)

5. Do I eat too much salt? (If the circulation is sluggish, salt tends to increase the retention of water in the body. Try using smaller quantities of sea salt.)

6. Do I eat too much fat? There may be many arguments as to which is better for you — vegetable oils or dairy fats – and there is no real doubt at all that too much fat of any sort is harmful. My advice is to cut down your total fat intake, make sure that any meat you eat is lean, and that you balance your consumption of fats between animal and dairy on the one hand and

vegetable on the other. As much as forty per cent of many people's total daily calorie intake is derived from fats, and this should be reduced to a maximum of twenty to twenty-five per cent.

Right, as you are determined to eat for health, now for slimming the Cider Vinegar way!

THREE RULES
FIRST RULE:
Start off your day by *sipping* two teaspoonsful of cider vinegar in a tumbler of cold or lukewarm water. Have it ready by the side of your bed.

SECOND RULE:
Sip a tumbler of water containing the two teaspoonsful of cider vinegar *during* each of the three main meals of the day – breakfast, lunch and dinner. Try to make your drink last the whole meal through. If you cut out any meal, have the cider vinegar drink instead.

THIRD RULE:
Chew your food thoroughly. This is to give the cider vinegar the greatest chance to act.

If you are fat or even a bit overweight, this change in your body did not happen in a week or two. You have grown larger gradually, perhaps over many years. *WARNING! Do not reduce too fast.* If you rush it, not only will your skin sag but you will become overtired and fractious.

Achieving the right weight is a wonderful thing to do. Be happy whilst you slim. This really is possible when you slim with cider vinegar.

Now for some experiences of those who have succeeded and now make cider vinegar a part of their daily routine:

Mrs E.D., an old age pensioner from Shrewsbury writes:

'I have taken 2 tsp. of cider vinegar with each meal for 8-9 months, not bothering when out or looking after guests. Last month I lost another 2 lb. making 17 lb. over the period.'

Mrs M.D., of Perthshire, Scotland. says:

'I have been taking cider vinegar daily for six months and have lost 21 pounds.'

It was Miss J.B. of Ripon, who said:

'Cider vinegar is a girth's best friend!'

This is an amusing truth which applies not only to girls but also to men. For example, Mr C.F-G., of Glamorgan, found he not only lost weight but improved in general health. A male nurse, Mr C.F., of Bournemouth, found the answer to be cider vinegar, after a long battle with obesity. Mr J.S. of Belfast, was embarrassed by his 'pot' when he went swimming but now he looks fine again.

As long as you keep the **THREE RULES** you can confidently expect to slim, even if you fail to reform your diet, but how much better to do both.

Miss S.B., of London, S.E.3, found that she could slim *without* that most difficult attribute – will-power! Mr A.H.E., of Frinton-On-Sea, said that cider vinegar worked wonders for him without any exercise at all, although my own view is that slimming comes with cider vinegar but a good shape from a mixture of heredity and exercise. If you were born with a tendency to podgy thighs there is always the possibility that when you slim enough to have gorgeous thighs, you will have a skinny neck or hollow cheeks. I am sure that slow slimming, the cider vinegar way, minimizes these problems, whereas rapid slimming aggravates them.

An extra bonus was pointed out to me by Mrs M.P., of Chesterfield, when she remarked that she had tried dozens of slimming methods without success but when she used the cider vinegar way it not only worked, it was economical. She was supported by very many others, including Mrs G.F., of Kings Norton, who said that cider vinegar lost weight for her without any diet at all.

In this connexion I would say that she is not quite right. You see, we are all on a diet, you, me, our friends. The problem is whether or not it is the right diet for you. It is not wise to generalize because human needs are a very personal thing. But one thing is certain, in many, many peoples' diet, cider vinegar is very effective indeed for the normalization of weight. So, if that is your problem, start right away. As I go about meeting people, I shall be very interested to hear how you progress.

ARTHRITIS AND RHEUMATISM

Arthritis

My interest in the cider vinegar therapy for arthritis was awakened many years ago when I found that one of my thumbs had suddenly become so weak that I could not lift a jug or a dinner plate. The Royal National Orthopaedic Hospital took X-rays and removed much blood for blood tests. I had osteo-arthritis. I mixed myself a 'natural cocktail' — a tumbler of warm water in which I dissolved two teaspoonsful each of cider vinegar and molasses and one of pure unblended honey. Within three months I was better and have not had a recurrence since, and that is about twenty-three years ago Spontaneous remissions are always possible. But in my mind a spontaneous remission is a result of the body winning a fight against disease, not just luck.

In the intervening years I have found people who do not get on with the mixture I used. They find cider vinegar alone or cider vinegar and honey the best for them. Others just use crude black molasses with good results, yet others fail to obtain relief, but in my experience among arthritics they are a minority.

The first point to remember is that if there has been a great change in the bone through calcium deposits caused by arthritis, then it is not at all likely that this will be altered. The second thing to remember is that 'a cure' is probably too much to hope for or to expect.

Look for control of symptoms, easing of pain and a reduction in the development of the condition. Keep as mobile as possible and above all do not give up hope. The longer you have had arthritis, the longer it is likely to be before you obtain a helpful result.

Charles Walker, an old friend of mine, related how, when he owned a Health Store in Birkenhead, an elderly man came in one day and danced round the shop. When questioned, he said he was not going crazy, he was demonstrating that he *could* dance. Two years before he had visited the store in a wheel-chair, crippled with arthritis. He had taken cider vinegar and molasses for two years and felt ten years younger! Not everyone can expect such results,

but they are at least a matter of common experience.
Dr Jarvis recommends for arthritis:

1. Two teaspoonsful cider vinegar and two of honey in a glass of water, taken at each meal, or if not acceptable, between meals.
2. On Monday, Wednesday and Friday add one drop of iodine at one meal to the mixture.
3. One kelp tablet at breakfast or at all three meals.
4. Avoidance of wheat foods and cereals, white sugar, citrus fruits, muscle meats such as beef, lamb and pork, as these produce an adverse reaction.

He says this regime helps rheumatoid arthritis, osteo-arthritis, bursitis and gout.

I have no quarrel with these procedures but wonder if the dietary restrictions in fact make much difference. As you will have read, I believe that the addition of molasses helps because of the great cleansing power of that food, so my recommendation for arthritis is:

1. On rising, two teaspoonsful of cider vinegar in a tumbler of water.
2. With each meal, two teaspoonsful each of cider vinegar and molasses with one of honey, sipped during the meal in a tumbler of water.
3. A natural vitamin and mineral supplement each day.
4. A diet very low in sugar and refined flour.

Mrs D.T. of Pinner, who has a spine that has had to be surgically fixed together, is now free from pain by following this treatment. After years of pain she finds the feeling of relief unbelievable.

Mr F.N. of Willenhall writes: 'not only has cider vinegar, honey and molasses helped my arthritis but for general health it is so good that people ask me where I get my energy from (I am 80 years old).'

Mr J.J. of Edinburgh says that he no longer requires the use of drugs or a collar since taking cider vinegar alone.

Mrs F.S. of London, S.E.11, found that although she is almost crippled with arthritis, cider vinegar was a great help in keeping it under control.

Mrs M.S. of Rotherham found that mixing cider vinegar with honey brought her quick relief, whereas Mrs M.H. of Tuffley, found that cider vinegar with molasses gave her the most effective relief from pain.

Mrs E.H. of Winchester writes: 'I have been an addict of cider vinegar since buying a Cyril Scott book many years ago. I have recommended the product to many friends especially sufferers from arthritis. My husband and I are approaching eighty years of age and neither of us have a twinge, and enjoy perfect health. We play bowls and do modern sequence dancing several times a week: My husband drinks his cider vinegar with lunch – calling it his dry white wine!'

When a doctor uses modern drugs in the treatment of arthritis he is involved with many problems such as controlling the side-effects of cortisone or the gastric problems of aspirin. You have none of these difficulties when employing the cider vinegar method, although it must be stated that in intractable cases the whole armoury of medicine in skilled hands is needed to make life tolerable for those who suffer from arthritis.

Do try to start treatment early on. In this way

you may much delay or permanently avoid the development of more serious symptoms and control your condition through safe and natural means.

Muscular Rheumatism

This is a muscular condition which may be caused by the build-up of poisons in the muscles or by the failure of the body to remove toxic wastes quickly enough. In general I have found that treatment as for arthritis is usually helpful. I must point out though that they are not the same, as arthritis affects joints and rheumatism the muscles. It tends to be aggravated by draughts and damp clothes.

Ordinary muscular rheumatism is not all that serious, especially if you look after yourself, avoiding excessive exertions to which you are not accustomed.

Mrs A.P. of Cardiff tells me that with cider vinegar alone she has had great relief from her muscular rheumatism.

Mrs K.M.C., who found great benefit for her condition, said she was told of it by a very old lady who had known the remedy for 80 years!

Mr J.M.N. of Barnstaple, was suffering frequently and now takes a dessertspoonful each of honey and cider vinegar in water so that it has become a way of life – without any more aches and pains. He goes on to say that his favourite cider vinegar is so mellow, mature and smooth tasting that it can be taken like wine without offending the stomach.

Gout

Although gout is often associated with rheumatism

in people's minds, it is likely that it is somewhat different in cause. Modern medicines relieve the acutely painful attack in a way no natural remedy can.

The cider vinegar, honey and molasses mixture is, in cases of gout, best taken half as strong and twice as often so that you have a pint of the weaker liquid at each meal.

Avoid port and red wine. (Pitt, the statesman, had gout at twenty-one but it is usually a problem of middle age.) Eat little muscle meat, no sardines or roe. Plenty of wholegrain foods and fresh fruit. If you really have to drink alcohol, whisky and water appears to be statistically preferable for there is a very low incidence of gout in Scotland.

NOSE AND THROAT DISORDERS

Colds

Not only does the common cold and its complications cause a great deal of time to be taken from work, it also usually makes the sufferer a misery to himself and a threat to others.

Professor Linus Pauling of the U.S.A. has written of the good effects of very large doses of vitamin C in the prevention and treatment of colds. This theory has been supported by recent trials in British and Canadian universities. Although the long-term physical effects of these large doses are not yet finally established, Professor Pauling believes that we all need more vitamin C than is customary and suggests we keep it on the table in powder form to sprinkle over our food and put into drinks. I find 1,000 milligrams (1 gram) of vitamin C a day very helpful but when exposed to colds or at the beginning of one, I increase the dose to 1 gram every three hours. This can, with great advantage, be taken in the cider vinegar drink.

The vitamin C therapy does not work with everyone. An American put on a play in London not long ago and the producer wished to avoid, as it was a winter opening, the problem of having colds among the cast. An actor who appeared in the show told me that in spite of injections of vitamin C, plus large daily doses of tablets, this was the only play he has ever appeared in which had to close down for several nights because of the epidemic of colds among cast and understudies alike! But it does work for most people, especially with cider vinegar, at least to minimize the symptoms. For others cider vinegar alone reduces the number of colds, probably by building up the general bodily strength.

Subsequent research has failed to conclusively confirm or deny the vitamin C story but I am still sure that it is a valuable aid at times of risk from infection. Several observers believe that natural vitamin C, which contains the bioflavanoids usually present in nature, is far more effective than pure chemical vitamin C, so if you are not having success with the cheaper synthetic product then try some of the excellent natural preparations you can find in health stores.

Coughs

If you have a mild cough it is a good idea to have a glass of double strength cider vinegar drink, that is, four teaspoonsful of cider vinegar to a glass of water. Swallow a few small sips slowly when the cough is aggravating. This often brings relief and at night permits sleep.

Mr T.B. of Hailsham, has rid himself of night cough after many months by means of this treatment.

Laryngitis

Cyril Scott recommends as a miraculous treatment, one teaspoonful of the cider vinegar to half a glass of water every hour for seven hours. It is also a valuable precautionary measure when you are exposed to infection. I find a little honey added to the mixture most helpful.

Sore Throat

The bacteria often responsible for sore throats prefer an alkaline environment and this may be the reason why the same treatment as for laryngitis works well. If my throat is sore or relaxed after too much talking and especially if I have to address a group of people or, as happened once, I was scheduled to make a television recording about health foods when my voice was not much more than a whisper, I find it essential to have a first-aid way of avoiding embarrassment even if only for a short time. This first-aid is a special gargle which gives instant relief that is usually maintained for up to three-quarters of an hour. To make it, take:

Special Gargle for the Throat

10 fl oz (275ml) cider vinegar
4 oz (100g) honey
1 oz (25g) red sage (garden sage, *Salvia officinalis*)
½ oz (15g) self-heal (*Prunella vulgaris*)

Heat the cider vinegar with the herbs until it is almost, but not quite, boiling. (Make sure that the pan is *not* aluminium.) Allow to cool slowly. Strain after twenty-four hours, add the honey, stir until dissolved, bottle and cap securely. Use two teaspoonsful in half a glass of water.

Catarrh

Many users have found cider vinegar to assist the clearance of catarrh. Take the basic drink of two teaspoonsful in a glass of water three times daily but, in addition, put a couple of inches of pure cider vinegar in a small stainless steel or enamel saucepan, simmer it gently and inhale the vapours for five or ten minutes. This procedure brings relief which often lasts up to eight hours.

Nose Bleeding

Because cider vinegar is an astringent it is worth trying in the same way as for catarrh in cases of persistent nose bleeding.

NERVES, CHOKING NERVOUS COUGH

The helpful effects of cider vinegar in many cases of insomnia due to tension are well recognized but an extension of this use as a relaxing beverage came to my notice recently and I cannot do better than quote from the letter written by Miss L.E.B. of Edinburgh:

'I would like to give you an unsolicited testimonial for cider vinegar, for it has literally given me a new lease of life. Although I had been on a course of molasses for six years, I thought I would start taking cider apple vinegar with my main meal.

For 30 years I have never had a single meal without CHOKING and going blue in the face. My throat would just close right up. Sometimes I could manage half-way through a meal, but it always ended up the same. Consequently, I lost friends, people stopped asking me out and I was a nuisance to myself and everyone else. During the war in the services I had to stand by and see someone else eating my rations because I could not swallow.

One night about a year and a half ago, I was sitting alone and eating my evening meal when it suddenly came to me *I was not choking any more*! I can never tell you what this meant to me – catch *me* going on a diet! Ever since, if I take two teaspoonsful in water with meals, I can eat everything that is put in front of me. In fact I like my food better if I take the vinegar with it – I can go anywhere, cafes, other people's homes. I have joined a Burn's Club and we have gone all over the place during the past 12 months and I have had no trouble at all. Perhaps, if you know of other sufferers like myself, recommend cider vinegar. The doctor said it was nerves but thanks to cider vinegar all is now well and I am making up for lost time.'

This very interesting report does demonstrate the profound balancing and normalizing effect of cider vinegar in a most human situation. When you are afflicted by nerves and tensions try not to resort to habit-forming and mentally exhausting drugs such as phenobarbitone. They are the cause of increasing national and international concern for, while they are a blessing to some who are suffering extreme pressures or tensions, they are too freely given in cases where a natural remedy, such as cider vinegar, will give relief without risk of any sort.

INSOMNIA AND ASTHMA

This section is about ordinary sleeplessness not resulting from pain or illness. Drugs do not usually *cure* insomnia. They just desensitize the mind for a while, often leaving a 'hang-over' next morning. I have written of the dangers of the indiscriminate use of powerful habit-forming drugs. Even less strong medicines can have their dangers. Think of the thalidomide children, for example.

Good sleep is nature's great restorative. Some people, as did Napoleon, are able to make do with three or four hours each night. For most of us, though, it occupies about one-third of our entire lives, so we had best learn to do it well.

The effects of sleep are felt on the majority of our bodily functions. The first sign is a deepening of the breathing and a slowing of the heart beat. The blood pressure falls. The body temperature drops by about half a Fahrenheit degree (or a quarter Centigrade). Your feet grow warmer and your hands colder. The sweat glands are very busy, so good ventilation is necessary. The blood supply to the brain does not decrease. Indeed, your brain is active at night. About an hour after you fall asleep, the pupils of your eyes move quite rapidly. This movement appears to be an essential component of really refreshing sleep and its onset and duration is delayed if sedative drugs are used.

What then can we learn from all this to help our slumbers? Firstly as night approaches, you must cultivate quite consciously a peaceful frame of mind. Think of good things and nice people. Some gentle music often helps. It will be good if you have taken a little exercise in the open air – a short walk, perhaps,brisk enough to tire you a little. Remember that people need differing amounts of sleep although this is inconvenient if your marriage partner needs twice (or half) as much as you do!

In any case, as you grow older you tend to need *less* sleep.

Next it is good to have a warm nourishing drink half-an-hour before retiring. Just before going to bed sip half a tumblerful of cider vinegar and honey, 2 teaspoonsful of each in warm water. Lie down, think pleasant thoughts, relax your body, starting at the toes and going right through the frame until the fingertips are relaxed – breathe deeply and regularly. Do not be worried about *not* sleeping – do not be worried about anything at all – there is nothing you can do to change things in the middle of the night anyway.

Make sure your bedroom is warm enough. Breathing very cold or damp air is bad for the chest and aggravates bronchitis, especially amongst senior citizens. They have, too, a peculiar problem. As the kidneys age, the water they pass to the bladder becomes less and less strong, so there is more of it! Drinking less is quite the worst thing to do. Your kidneys *need* the water to carry on the process of excretion. Just resign yourself to maybe having to rise a couple of times in the night. Take a few more sips of the honey/cider vinegar combination and go peacefully back to sleep again. Many older people read a book in the night or do a few little chores. Just make sure, when you leave your bed, that you do not become chilled.

If you cannot sleep because of pain, grief or

illness, then you may need the care and advice of a qualified practitioner who is in a position to advise you upon your individual needs.

ASTHMA

In times passed this used to be called the Devil's Disease. Happily, the majority of sufferers are now able to obtain relief from the worst symptoms and often, when the cause is an allergy, a complete cure. Yet others have a spontaneous cessation, or it may be supplanted by hay fever. On the other hand, asthma, although it is most common amongst children and young adults, sometimes does not appear until the forties.

During an attack the person has a feeling of tightness in the throat and neck with perhaps a frightening feeling of suffocation. Breathing is difficult, especially breathing out. Sticky mucus, which later becomes thin, is coughed up when the attack usually ends with a feeling of extreme tiredness.

It is caused by a sudden reduction in diameter of the small tubes in the lungs combined with the production of a lot of mucus. The patient wheezes because of the difficulty of forcing air out through these narrow tubes.

Why the tubes become narrow is a more difficult question. There are three recognized reasons: firstly, an attack of bronchitis sometimes starts asthma off; secondly, asthma can be an allergic reaction to a particular pollen or type of dust, for example; thirdly, it can be inherited from forbears with asthma or hay fever or nettle rash.

The cider vinegar treatment with honey (2 teaspoonsful of each in a tumbler of water thrice daily) has produced some remarkable results which are presently the subject of long-term experiments. It is certainly worth trying but also it is important for the sufferer to avoid aggravating his own condition by adopting a life as free as possible from stresses and strains and by not placing himself in the way of any causative factors which experience has previously indicated. Smoking is best abandoned. Fatness, or even slight overweight, throws an excessive strain onto the body during an attack, so slim! Happily, an asthmatic lady usually avoids attacks when expecting a child.

Mr M. McK. of Suffolk 'cured' his long-standing asthma by cider vinegar in water *without* honey, but as most of the experiments have been done with honey, that should be the first preference.

HAY FEVER

The sufferer has what appears to be a very bad summer cold, but there is no infection. Hay fever is caused by sensitization to proteins. We all tend to reject protein of a sort different to our own, that is why tissue transplants are so difficult to carry out effectively. The air is full of pollen protein on a hot summer's day to which many people are acutely sensitive. They pray for rain to keep the pollen count to a bearable level.

Special nasal sprays are sometimes used but these often cause permanent damage to the delicate lining of the nose.

Hay fever is rare in very small infants and tends to reduce in intensity as middle age approaches although it does not often go entirely.

An exception, which is an example well worth following, is Mrs L.E.G. of Thorpe Bay, who obtained a complete cure by taking, once a day throughout the season, 2 teaspoonsful each of honey and cider vinegar in a glassful of water and, at the same time, cutting out all sugar.

When she wrote to me she had been fine for eleven years, having been a very bad sufferer for the previous thirty-four years. Her experience was published in the *Sunday Express*. She subsequently received no less than 4,000 letters and replied to each one! This at least must recommend the therapy! Many of those who tried the method were as successful as she, others were not, but in any case general health and resistance will have been improved.

Miss C.J.P. of Southend-on-Sea writes:

'I recommend cider vinegar to my friends with hay fever, rheumatism, etc. During last summer's hay fever season I stopped people in the street in Southend High Street telling them about the cider vinegar and honey mixture whenever I saw anyone sneezing obviously from hay fever. Following the discussion on the BBC "You and Yours" programme about hay fever I wrote to them telling them that cider vinegar and honey kept me free this summer. Two days later my letter was read out on this programme. Since thousands must listen to the programme I would imagine many hay fever sufferers are now taking the mixture as I suggested – that is one dose at night all the year round.'

BEAUTY

The skin, like the eyes, is one of the most obvious

places to look for signs of tiredness, age, worry or poor general health. Healthy skin has a bloom and elasticity which, with care, lasts into old age. I do not believe that cider vinegar will bring about a miraculous transformation but those who take it in the usual way for other purposes frequently report a great general improvement in skin tone and appearance which causes them to continue with regular doses.

The reason may lie in the inner cleanliness which is a feature of the treatment. Yellowing eyes are a sign of 'liverishness' and in mild cases cider vinegar taken internally is a great help.

Hair is dead except at the point of growth in the hair follicle but to remain in the best condition it is important to give the scalp a favourable environment.

It happens that shampoo is usually alkaline. The scalp, on the other hand, is acid and protected by natural fats. Nature's protection is washed away allowing skin to become scaly and the scalp dry. The balance can be restored by using a cider vinegar rinse after you have shampooed your hair. Many hair stylists use this rinse in preference to the well-known beer rinse because they prefer the cosmetic result. When you add to this the benefit of the treatment to the condition of the scalp, you have discovered a reason why so many use cider vinegar externally as well as internally.

There are several ways of using cider vinegar as a beauty treatment, but as few users would wish to smell with an odour more reminiscent of a fish and chip shop than a beauty parlour it is a good plan to make a pleasant infusion. My favourite is:

ROSEMARY AND CIDER VINEGAR SKIN LOTION

Place 1 oz (25g) of fresh rosemary or ½ oz (15g) dried rosemary in a saucepan with half-a-pint (275ml) of water (rain water is best). Bring slowly to the boil, simmer gently for ten minutes, strain, mix with half-a-pint of cider vinegar. When cool, pour in bottles that can be securely sealed. Store in a dark, cool place.

This makes a fine general purpose lotion. If you wish, by all means add a few drops of eau de-Cologne or perfume. Also other herbs can be used or rose petals even, but rosemary is good for the hair.

You can use the lotion in the following ways:

For a Hair Conditioner – A little poured into the palms of the hands, rubbed vigorously into the scalp with the finger tips.

For a Hair Rinse – A tablespoonful in the final rinsing water makes a wonderful cosmetic rinse.

For the Skin – Dab the lotion on the face very gently, working out from the wrinkles and sagging places.

For Swellings – Some remarkable results are achieved with this lotion or, in fact, just plain cider vinegar, in cases of swellings caused by fatigue, long standing or strained muscles. Apply liberally every hour until the swelling reduces. If you can, make a cold compress from the lotion. This has a very good effect on severe strains. Many people's feet and legs swell whilst travelling. The cider vinegar treatment, both internally and externally, is a valuable aid.

VARICOSE VEINS

These must be cared for by a properly qualified person but they are, nevertheless, often most uncomfortable. As Mrs V.M. of Huddersfield wrote: 'Cider Vinegar gives me great relief from varicose veins.' The treatment cannot be considered in any way a cure but has a beneficial effect nonetheless.

FINGER-NAILS

A doctor can often tell much from an examination of the nails. The white spots which sometimes appear are generally due to a deficiency of calcium. It is a frequent observation that these spots disappear when cider vinegar is being used. This is not because it is a provider of calcium in large amounts, although an appreciable proportion is present, but because it helps the body to make more effective use of the calcium in the diet.

Growing children need more calcium than adults and usually obtain it from milk. Older people, on the other hand, find efficient use of sufficient calcium a help in preserving strong bones and in mending them following a fracture.

The nails, then, can show the effects of the cider vinegar treatment in the elimination of white spots. At the same time, some users' have reported a general strengthening of thin and brittle nails. Mrs M.M. of Kingsbury, who was a sufferer from generally weak nails, found relief for the first time after many unsuccessful experiments and her nails are now completely restored. This cannot take place overnight – even a year may be needed before results are apparent, especially with older sufferers from weak nails.

EYES

I have mentioned the better appearance of the eyes frequently noticed as an effect of the treatment. So often we find the physical outward attributes of a user improve as a direct result of the internal benefit of cider vinegar

Mr E.A.K of Portsmouth, reports that he found that a cataract which was forming in one of his eyes stopped progressing by any means so rapidly as before when he took cider vinegar regularly. On the other hand, it must be confessed that this is not a common finding, although not unique, and it may have been a spontaneous slowing-down.

SHINGLES

This is caused by the same virus as chicken pox as parents who have never had chicken pox sometimes find to their anguish when infected by their children. It causes burning pain usually along the path of a nerve. The pain is generally gone with the rash after about a week but occasionally persists. Sufferers, such as Mr W.C.F. of Lancing, have found neat cider vinegar dabbed regularly upon the sore areas to give far more relief than any medicament. The pain abates quite soon after each treatment but returns after an hour or so, when the application needs to be repeated.

THE DIGESTION

Many digestive disorders arise from a relatively small number of defects. Sometimes the bacteria which work to break down our food for us are of the wrong kind. The problem of too much acidity is not as common as the sellers of patent alkaline medicines may have you believe. In fact, the *reverse* is often true – sufferers from indigestion may not have enough acid.

When you eat food it goes through a first process of digestion in the mouth where the starches are turned, during the chewing process, into sugar by the enzymes in the saliva. Because chewing helps to break down the food and stimulate the flow of saliva it is important to chew thoroughly. Many of those who live on grain diets, and Eastern philosophers, say chewing each mouthful forty times produces the best results. For my part, I am rather bored a long time before that!

The human saliva is usually alkaline but the active enzyme works best in a slightly acid medium, so we have found our first indication of the value of the cider vinegar drink in that it assists the maintenance of the desired acidity.

After the food has been formed into a conveniently sized portion you swallow it and it descends the eight or nine inches to the stomach which is a collecting sack for the food you eat. The digestive process now carries on a further stage in the stomach. The gastric juices contain about 0.4 per cent of free hydrochloric acid together with enzymes which make the food liquid. Harmful bacteria and other organisms are usually made harmless whilst the food is in the stomach.

Digestion and absorption of the nutrients continues in the twenty-two feet long small intestine where there are more enzymes and a lot of valuable and essential bacteria which help to break down food into substances which can be absorbed by the body.

These bacteria appear to find, as animal results have shown, much benefit from cider vinegar. One theory, as I mention elsewhere, is that because cider vinegar contains both a high potassium content and acetic acid in apparently balanced amounts, the body is able to convert these raw materials in an entirely natural way into a substance which checks the growth of unwelcome bacteria, allowing the useful types to become more vigorous.

Water is absorbed into the body in the four feet of large intestine where waste matter is accumulated, prior to elimination.

Research by distinguished doctors, including a Fellow of the Royal Society, Dr Denis Burkitt, and his colleague the surgeon, Mr Neil Painter, has shown beyond reasonable doubt that for a really healthy digestive system it is necessary to have a quantity of cereal or vegetable fibre daily. The simplest way of taking this is to consume two level teaspoons of bran each day. This can be mixed with a little of the cider vinegar drink or added to your food. The results are remarkable provided the bran treatment is carried on indefinitely.

Having taken care of the general condition of your digestive organs, the specific effects of cider vinegar are themselves of the greatest interest and value.

INDIGESTION

As Mrs D.A. of Folkestone says, 'Until I took a glassful of cider vinegar drink with each meal I did not know what it was to experience a meal free from pain and subsequent discomfort.'

Mrs A.W. of Monmouth suffered from flatulence especially when eating pastry. She found complete relief by adding one teaspoonful of the vinegar to her pastry mix.

Mr R.E. actually suffered from indigestion due to acidity yet found a daily cider vinegar drink, in spite of being itself acid, an effective answer.

After excessive or unwise eating or drinking the high potassium content is probably a factor in the settling effect obtained by taking the cider vinegar drink. Miss K.S. went on further when she said that she found cider vinegar allowed indulgence without indigestion!

CONSTIPATION

This distressing condition cannot be good for you because of the pressures created in the intestine when 'forcing' is necessary. I have said that bran is an essential part of this treatment, but cider vinegar is also a great help.

Laxatives are not very good for you, besides being expensive, so try a glassful of water containing 2 teaspoonsful of cider vinegar on rising, during the main meal of the day and before retiring. If this, plus two tablespoonsful of bran each day does not solve your problem by the end of a month, then I would advise your seeking qualified help and advice.

DIARRHOEA

If diarrhoea alternates with constipation you must seek medical assistance, for it is just possible that this is an early warning that all is not well with your gut.

Strawberries affect some people, so do travelling, emotional disturbance and certain conditions or illnesses. The cure is to rectify the cause where this is possible. On the other hand, most diarrhoea is an unfortunate and temporary inconvenience for which cider vinegar is a good first-aid treatment. As one result of diarrhoea is the elimination of much of the water that is usually absorbed by the large intestine, you need plenty of fluids, two or three *extra* pints a day. Add *one* teaspoonful of the vinegar to each half pint (275ml). Sometimes a kaolin mixture, B.P.C., helps, but the concensus of opinion in simple cases not associated with illness is against most of the travellers' preventive tablets containing clioquinol sold by chemists because of the occasional side-effects.

If an infection is the cause of the problem then you must have the infection treated. The cider vinegar drink can safely be taken in addition to any treatment that is prescribed. Drink plenty of fluids to avoid dehydration.

HICCOUGHS

This occurs when your diaphragm is not synchronized properly with the flap which prevents you swallowing air into the stomach. It can arise from a variety of causes. There is a hot, spiced Persian dish called a patia which often starts me off!

Normally it goes away within the hour, unless it is due to some more serious condition, when the underlying cause should be located and treated. Hiccoughs can be tiring, so it is usual to seek aid if it persists for more than four hours.

The cider vinegar first-aid treatment is to sip, very slowly a teaspoonful of undiluted cider vinegar. This usually brings about an immediate cure. If not, try breathing in and out of a paper bag for a minute or two. This creates carbon dioxide which stimulates the breathing centre.

HEARTBURN

A burning sensation behind the breastbone an hour or so after meals is often found to diminish or vanish when cider vinegar is taken with the meal.

HEART CONDITIONS

Heart disease is the main killer of people in the prime of life. Men are vulnerable after the age of thirty-five. Women are usually not likely to have an attack until after the 'change', although the rate is rising, especially for women 'on the pill'.

There is no single cause of this curse of Western civilization, which is only rarely encountered amongst those who live on a natural unprocessed diet, but prevention is easier than cure. Perhaps we know half the causes, so to keep to the rules substantially reduces your risk.

Rules to avoid Heart Attacks

1. If you are not slim, become slim (see section on slimming).
2. Avoid sugar and foods made with sugar.
3. Avoid hard fats such as animal fat, coconut and palm oils. Replace them with unsaturated soft fats, such as sunflower seed oil, safflower, soya, corn, olive and fish oils. Cut down total fat intake.
4. Take enough exercise to become gently breathless each day; walk upstairs instead of using the lift.
5. Give up smoking.
6. Avoid constipation by taking bran and cider vinegar (see page 58). Sometimes older people temporarily increase blood pressure through straining, with fatal results.

7. Keep work, recreation, rest and holidays in a sensible balance, after all if you literally work yourself to death you will not be of much use to your family or community.

8. Eat a balanced, mixed diet, taking care not to overcook vegetables or to use too much water.

9. Avoid excessive salt (sodium chloride), the element sodium *in excess* increases the tendency of some people to high blood pressure. Use a little sea salt.

10. Try to have several small meals each day, not one huge feast which could throw a strain onto the body by increasing greatly the amount of fat in the blood stream.

From the foregoing it is plain that cider vinegar cannot be claimed to prevent, or for that matter to cure, heart troubles or allied disorders. Nevertheless, it can play a part in helping you to achieve or maintain the right weight. Additionally, some individuals find it does give them relief from certain symptoms.

ANGINA

Angina is a condition in which the arteries of the heart do not always pass enough blood. This gives rise to a sometimes suffocating pain in the upper chest which often also affects the left arm and the neck. This is similar to the type of pain often occurring in a coronary heart attack but, with rest, it passes off. Doctors give nitroglycerin tablets which must be chewed and give almost immediate relief. Patients who look after themselves have a good outlook and future.

Mr R.R. of Kemsing found the cider vinegar drink taken regularly lessened the severity of the attack. But I agree with Mr E.J. of Blackpool, who, as a sufferer, takes the cider vinegar treatment in order to keep his weight down and so improve his anginal condition.

HIGH BLOOD PRESSURE

This is also called hypertension. Sufferers benefit considerably by adopting the ten rules for avoiding heart attacks.

In their own cases, Mrs C.W. of Huddersfield and Mrs F.W. of Newtown found that the cider vinegar drink three times daily helped keep blood pressure down. This is likely to be because of an improvement in their general condition through the treatment.

CRAMP

Cramp is quite common amongst the middle-aged and elderly. It may arise because the muscles suffer from a building up of poisonous wastes which the circulation does not take away with enough speed. A number of sufferers have told me that the cider drink, preferably with honey in warm water, taken before retiring, reduces the frequency of attacks.

BURNS

Use pure, undiluted cider vinegar straight from the bottle to relieve the pain and soreness of minor burns.

Modern treatment for burns advocates very rapid cooling with lots of cold water as soon as a burn occurs. This is even more important when clothes are either burnt or wettened with a hot liquid. Pour cold water over the clothes at once. If it is a bad burn, always summon medical aid. Keep the patient warm and rested with something to drink. Do not remove clothing from, or otherwise disturb, the burnt area. Minor burns benefit from the cider vinegar treatment. When possible, it is best to leave them exposed to the air, provided that the skin is intact.

SUNBURN

The same general rules apply here as for ordinary burns. The cider vinegar dabbed on is most soothing. Really serious cases require medical help. Although cider vinegar is very good for treating sunburn, it is in no sense a preventive. A properly prepared filtering oil or lotion and a good deal of caution are both needed for a really happy holiday in the sun.

TEETH AND MOUTH

I must confess to having little personal experience of cider vinegar for the teeth but Cyril Scott, who still had a good few teeth in his nineties recommends the use of cider vinegar, one teaspoon in water night and morning, as a mouth wash. He says that the teeth should be brushed with the solution and that cider vinegar drinkers had unusually white teeth.

Scott mentions that two tablespoonsful of the vinegar to a kettle of water which is allowed to stand for a time allows the lime deposits to come away when the water is poured off, or it can be more easily scraped away without damaging the inner surface of the kettle.

He uses this as an analogy for dental use and I would be interested to hear from successful users for this purpose.

Mouth ulcers and sores also benefit from the

mouth wash; and for a tendency towards bleeding gums the mouth wash is helpful in addition to the cider vinegar treatment three times a day.·

CHAPTER FIVE

CIDER VINEGAR IN THE KITCHEN

If, like me, you are convinced of the health advantages of cider vinegar, then the logical next step is to use it as much as possible. The kitchen offers many wonderful opportunities to use cider vinegar in ways which are a compliment to your good taste.

The chef of one of the most distinguished hotels in London renowned for its cuisine, uses cider vinegar for its flavour in preference to wine or malt vinegar.

My family is not vegetarian, although we much respect the ethical ideals of our vegetarian friends. We are, on the other hand, believers in eating whole foods free so far as possible from any chemical additive. This happily permits gourmet cooking, which is a hobby of mine.

When my son Carl was seven or eight years old he often went shopping with me and would not let me buy anything to eat until he had read the list of ingredients to check that there were no synthetics. We still do that now, and I strongly commend the practice to you all, especially if you are able to avoid the occasional embarrassment I used to suffer when another shopper bought some instant wonder causing the voice of my son to rise in powerful protest pointing out to me and to all men the error of her ways! Now he is much older and away at school the main problem is finding enough of the right sort of foods, especially wholemeal bread, for a good diet. Nevertheless, the powerful basis for health that a good diet gave him during his first thirteen years seems to allow him to manage well with a less than ideal diet from time to time.

This cooking section sets out to let you into some of the delightful and varied uses we have for cider vinegar in our home. It includes some excellent additional recipes from other well-tried sources which are acknowledged in their due place.

Please remember that cider vinegar does sometimes form 'mother of vinegar' if the cap is not replaced tightly. If you are buying a gallon for economic reasons, it is not necessarily going to keep without some possibility of deterioration for a year or more, as some users expect. Six months is a fair life for a large bottle. Even then it is best to decant the gallon size into very clean half or one pint strongly stoppered bottles if you wish to use it over a longish period.

BASIC VINEGARS
Herbal or spiced vinegars are delightful to 'spike' the flavour of savoury dishes. You can also store herbs for the winter in a far more aromatic state than by drying them (although dry herbs have very many uses) by putting them tightly packed into a jar of cider vinegar. When you need the herb; just shake it dry and use in the way you prefer.

For the flavoured vinegars I find it best to buy sufficient small sized bottles of cider vinegar to provide one for each variety. Be sure to stick an appropriate label on after you have prepared the vinegar. It would be rather a shock to use chilli vinegar as a mouth wash!

BASIC METHOD

The basic methods are similar, except when specified. You remove a little vinegar if necessary, add the appropriate flavouring, re-seal and leave for a few days or a week before using. There is not normally any need to remove the herbs before use, in fact the flavour improves with age. The quantities are right for a 10 to 13 oz (275 to 375ml) bottle.

Celery Vinegar – Chop a $\frac{1}{4}$ lb (100g) of cleaned root and white stalk, leave for a month. Or use $\frac{1}{4}$ oz (7$\frac{1}{2}$g) celery seed instead. A pinch of seed is sometimes preferred in the first recipe. Good with salads.

Chilli Vinegar – Use one or two whole hot red or green chillies. One of each is nice. Dried chillies will do, but are not so full of flavour. Wonderful with fish dishes, curries and oysters.

Cucumber Vinegar – Chop 3 oz (75g) of cucumber, including the skin, together with a shallot or small onion with a crushed peppercorn. Very fragrant and refreshing with salads and cold meat.

Fennel Vinegar – Slice two outside leaves of fennel. You can also add some parsley if you like. Good with mutton and fish.

Fines Herbes Vinegar – This is a famous French general purpose flavoured vinegar. Excellent as a basis for a salad dressing. Use one half-teaspoonful each of whole peppercorns, tarragon and basil, the grated skin of a small lemon, a pinch each of savory, thyme, sea salt and raw sugar. One chopped shallot or a little onion, a scrape of dried horseradish, a small pinch of pimento and of crushed chopped bay leaf, one leaf of rosemary. This takes several months but is worth it! If you find this vinegar a little strong, then divide the contents of the first bottle into another.

Garlic Vinegar — The old recipe says that this is best made between Midsummer and Michaelmas, but that was before we could import garlic so easily. Some do not like the smell or flavour. I like both and believe it helps bring out most savoury flavours. Garlic is said to be good for you — never mind what the others say! Peel, chop and add one ounce (25g) of fresh garlic. Shake the bottle each day for ten days, then strain and re-bottle. You need use only a few drops at a time.

Horseradish and Chilli Vinegar — A powerful one, this! Use one ounce (25g) of grated horseradish, a teaspoonful of sea salt, a saltspoonful of dried ginger root, a pinch of cayenne pepper and a whole hot chilli.

Nasturtium Vinegar — Quite a piquant and unusual flavour comes from using a handful of freshly gathered nasturtium flowers, one clove, two peppercorns, a hint of crushed garlic and one chopped shallot (or a little onion). This is best kept for a month or two before using.

Rosemary Vinegar (Italian style) — Use a large sprig each of rosemary and of peppermint, together with a half teaspoonful of chopped angelica root.

Shallot Vinegar – Use 4 oz (100g) of chopped shallots. A large onion will do instead but the flavour is not as good.

Spiced Vinegar – In this case the spices need to be simmered with a very little of the vinegar. This is then added when cool to the rest and allowed to mature for a week. It is best then sieved and re-bottled. Use half a teaspoonful each of crushed chillies, pimento and coriander with a quarter teaspoonful each of cloves, ginger root, mustard powder and black pepper.

Tarragon Vinegar – Known to the French as *estragon*, tarragon is perhaps the most French of all herbs. It is strong, so you do not need to use much. Without doubt tarragon is the best herb to go with chicken but as tarragon vinegar it is used in the finest French dressings. Put a few fresh branches into the vinegar and it is soon ready for use. In this instance it is never a good idea to remove the tarragon as the vinegar drains away as you pour it. If you have no tarragon in your garden grow the variety called True French. Russian tarragon is rather less good.

SALAD DRESSINGS
There are not many attractive undressed things and salads are no exception. The variety you can use is a delight to the palate. The cook has the pleasure of deciding which will suit both the guests and the salad.

I find olive oil has a rather heavy and dominating flavour which does not attract me, but you may certainly use it if you like it. Use a first pressing olive oil in that case. Otherwise you will note that I have listed corn oil. This is because it is a good, moderately priced oil without much tendency to rancidity. It has a high content of the valuable unsaturated fats. You can equally well substitute corn oil by soya, safflower or sunflower oils.

Basic French Dressing

   3 parts corn oil
   1 part cider vinegar

Mix and add to the salad just before serving so that every leaf is shining. Many French people would use 6 parts oil to 1 part cider vinegar but that is too oily for my taste.

Tarragon Dressing
As above, using tarragon cider vinegar instead of the plain sort.

My Favourite Dressing
We have evolved this which our guests seem to like — it took a long time to get it right.

At least an hour before the meal (or the day before if you wish) mix:

   3 tablespoonsful corn oil
   1 tablespoonful cider vinegar
  · a squeeze of lemon juice
   one large crushed clove of garlic
   a turn of freshly ground black pepper
   a pinch of raw sugar
   a pinch of mustard powder
   some mixed herbs (see below)

Add to the salad after a brisk mix either at table or just before serving. Never use so much that there is a lot of free dressing at the bottom of the salad bowl.

For the mixed herbs I keep two assortments of dried herbs in screw-topped jars. They are slightly different from each other. I use whichever I happen to fancy. They are:

Herb Mix (A)
Parsley, tarragon, lemon balm, chervil, chives, dill, thyme, basil.

Herb Mix (B)
Parsley, dill, celery leaf flakes and tarragon.

The herbs are listed in roughly descending order of quantity, first largest, last least.

Yogurt Salad Dressing

This is good as it comes or can have herbs or garlic added as you wish. Blend or whisk thoroughly:

> 1 small carton of plain yogurt then,
> using the carton as a measure
> half a carton cider vinegar
> half a carton corn oil

Vinaigrette Dressings

These come in a wonderful assortment of flavours. The basic dressing is:

> 6 tablespoonsful corn oil
> 2 tablespoonsful cider vinegar
> 1 teaspoonful chopped capers
> 1 tablespoonful chopped onion
> ·1 tablespoonful herbs in the mixture, 2 parts parsley to one each of chervil, tarragon and chives.
> a pinch of sea salt and pepper

Mix thoroughly. Use with avocado pears, asparagus, cauliflowers, game, meat or salad. The quantities can be halved or doubled, as required.

Vinaigrette with Eggs
There are two good ways of doing this, the first is best for chicken and fish, the second with salads.

Recipe (A)
   Soft boil 2 eggs (3 minutes).
   Scoop out the yolks, add these to the basic dressing and mix. Chop the white, stir it gently in.

Recipe (B)
   Use 2 hard-boiled chopped eggs, a little chopped gherkin and a little chopped lemon peel with the basic dressing. Stir gently.

Curried Vinaigrette
Add a teaspoonful of curry powder and an extra-finely chopped onion to the basic dressing. Allow to stand several hours before use.

Blue Cheese Dressing
Add from one to four tablespoonsful of crumbled dry Roquefort, Stilton, Danish Blue or Gorgonzola.

Nutty Salad Dressing
This is rather good with cold rice, or with chicory and other full-flavoured salads.

   2 tablespoonsful cider vinegar
   1 tablespoonful corn oil
   ¼ teaspoonful mustard powder
   1 saltspoonful mixed herbs (see above)
   1 egg yolk (raw)
   1 tablespoonful mixed coarsely chopped nuts
   1 small chopped apple

You need to add the nuts and apple after the other

ingredients have been thoroughly beaten together.
If you find the dressing a little sharp you can add a
touch of honey or of raw sugar to taste.

Banana Dressing
Unusual but an interesting change especially with
chicory.

> 2 tablespoonsful cider vinegar
> 1 tablespoonful corn oil
> 1 tablespoonful natural yogurt
> a pinch of sea salt and pepper
> a big pinch of mixed herbs
> banana (1 or more depending on the number of people)

Crush the banana with a fork until it becomes
smooth and creamy. Mix well in firstly the yogurt,
then the herbs. Next add the cider vinegar and the
oil. Mix very briskly. Finely chopped ham is a good
addition if you like it.

I am sure you will enjoy these cider vinegar
dressings and have pleasure discovering and trying
many others.

SAUCES
At home we enjoy the extra fullness of flavour and
delicate aroma which comes from using cider
vinegar in our sauces. Some of the old, traditional
recipes are particularly interesting and much
enjoyed. A few new ideas bring excitement – but
first one of the basic sauces which, although from
simple ingredients, requires a little care for good
results:

Sauce Hollandaise
This is best made 'finger-tip hot' or just as hot as

the finger-tip will stand. Over-heating will produce bad scrambled egg. Take:

8 oz (225g) butter
4 egg yolks
1 tablespoonful cider vinegar
a pinch of sea salt and freshly ground pepper
1 tablespoonful cold water.

Boil a large saucepan about one-third full of water. While it is heating, cut the butter into some twenty small pieces. Put the water, cider vinegar and the egg yolks into a small enamel or stainless steel saucepan, whisk in the salt and pepper whilst continuing to whisk, gently lower the pan into the boiling water.

As soon as the yolks become thicker, take the pan from the water, put in one of the pats of butter. Whisk again to a smooth cream, add another pat of butter. If it melts whisk again to a cream. Go on until the butter does melt. Return the pan to the water until it just melts. Do not stop beating. Do this until all the butter has been used. When this has happened again warm-up the sauce, still beating, until it is finger-tip hot. Serve immediately in a warm sauce-boat.

I like this on the huge tender asparagus spears, beloved of the Germans, which are eatable from tip to base – but Hollandaise is good with many vegetables.

I hope you have not become discouraged by the difficulties of that one, but the sauces become easier from now on!

Aïoli Sauce

If you believe that garlic is good for you, this sauce is a way of making sure everyone knows. It is made to the consistency of mayonnaise. In Marseille they call it 'Friday Sauce' because it is used on fish. We like it with boiled potatoes, French beans and hard-boiled eggs, as well.

> 4 cloves garlic (or 2 for each person)
> 2 egg yolks (or 1 each)
> 8 fl oz (225ml) corn oil
> sea salt, pepper, cider vinegar

Either crush the garlic to a paste or put it in a blender with the egg yolks and salt. Add the oil *very* gradually, whisking or blending all the time. Stop when you have made a thick mayonnaise. Add pepper and cider vinegar to taste. We use about a tablespoon of the vinegar. Lord Burntwood tells me that *Aïoli* was created because of the need to disguise the strong salted fish brought to France by the Newfoundland fishing boats from the eighteenth century onwards.

Mayonnaise

It is possible nowadays to buy ready-made mayonnaise containing cider vinegar, sunflower oil and fresh egg yolks. This is as good as home made, but here is how to do it yourself.

> 3 egg yolks
> ½ teaspoonful sea salt
> ½ teaspoonful mustard powder
> 1 tablespoonful boiling water
> 10 fl oz (275ml) corn or sunflower seed oil
> 1 tablespoonful cider vinegar
> (*Tarragon* cider vinegar is best)

Have all the ingredients and the bowl at room temperature. Put egg yolks into the bowl and beat for about a minute until they thicken. Add the cider vinegar, sea salt and mustard. Beat for one more minute. Keep beating steadily and then add the oil a drop at a time. If you go too fast it will curdle. (If that happens start again with another yolk and a little oil and add this to the failure to revive it.) As you add more oil it will become easier.

After almost a half has been combined, you can increase the oil to a thin stream. When the oil has been used, beat in a tablespoonful of boiling water. This helps to prevent it separating. Taste to see if you have enough seasoning. Many people find that they prefer two or three tablespoonsful of cider vinegar. If you do this in the blender you need 1 whole egg and 2 yolks.

Having made your mayonnaise, or bought it, you can try lots of good variations.

Louis Sauce (for shellfish)

6 fl oz (175ml) (about 1 cupful) mayonnaise
2 tablespoonsful grated onion
2 fl oz (50ml) chilli sauce (see separate recipe)
2 tablespoonsful chopped parsley
3 fl oz (75ml) whipped double cream
a dash of cayenne

Stir together. Allow to stand for about two hours in a cool place to develop the flavour.

Ravigote Sauce (one of the best for cold vegetables or shellfish)

6 fl oz (175ml) mayonnaise
1 tablespoonful cider vinegar
1 teaspoonful mustard powder
1 chopped shallot
1 tablespoonful chopped capers
1 teaspoonful chopped tarragon

Mix gently. Serve cold.

Thousand Island (the best for prawn cocktail)

> 6 fl oz (175ml) mayonnaise
> 1 dash Tabasco sauce or
> 1 tablespoonful chilli sauce
> 1 tablespoonful cider vinegar
> 4 tablespoonsful tomato *purée* (from a tube is easy)

Stir together and chill before use.

Tartare Sauce

> 6 fl oz (175ml) mayonnaise
> 1 chopped hard-boiled egg yolk
> 1 medium-sized grated onion
> 1 tablespoonful chopped chives
> 1 teaspoonful fine chopped parsley
> 1 tablespoonful chopped capers
> 2 teaspoonsful cider vinegar

Mix well and allow to stand an hour before using.

Mayonnaise Chantilly

> 6 fl oz (175ml) mayonnaise
> 2 fl oz (50ml) whipped cream

Sir the two gently together.

You can invent your own. Amongst tried favourites are mayonnaise with any of the following for 6 fl oz (175ml):

> Asparagus, 2 oz (50g) chopped, drained
> Chives, 1 tablespoonful chopped
> Curry powder, 2 teaspoonsful (best if cooked before adding with a little oil and onion)
> Cheese (add 3 tablespoonsful grated cheese and some paprika, thin with cream)
> Chutney (drain first)
> Chilli powder (not too much, ¼ teaspoonful to try)
> Green (coloured with juice crushed from 4 tablespoonsful

watercress, 2 tablespoonsful parsley)
Mustard (add 2 tablespoonsful mustard powder)
Paprika, 1 teaspoonful (very pretty rose colour)
Verte (pound up 1 teaspoonful chives, 1 tablespoonful chervil, 1 tablespoonful tarragon, 1 tablespoonful spinach with 1 tablespoonful water. Squeeze through muslin into mayonnaise.)

Sauce Béarnaise

This king of French sauces, surely the best accompaniment to steak, was accidentally left out of my first draft of this book. Thankfully Lord Burntwood noted the omission of this favourite of his before it was too late!

2 tablespoonsful cider vinegar
1 teaspoonful chopped shallots (or onions)
6 peppercorns
A bay leaf
2 teaspoonsful tarragon
2 teaspoonsful chervil
¼ cupful (approximately) gravy or stock
1½ oz (40g) butter
2 egg yolks

First of all you boil up the shallots and peppercorns, bay leaf, and half of the chervil and tarragon in the cider vinegar until it has reduced to half. Strain and reserve the liquid. Put a double saucepan on and boil it fast (a basin in an ordinary saucepan will do if you give it time to heat through). Mix the egg yolks with a little of the stock and put in the double boiler, stirring constantly. Still stirring, add the butter, a small piece at a time. When the mixture has thickened, add the rest of the stock and then the cider vinegar liquor. Finally, stir in the rest of the chervil and tarragon and serve piping hot.

Chilli Sauce

This is very hot, but marvellous in small amounts or as an addition to other sauces.

    6 hot red chillies, chopped finely, including seeds
    4 large onions, chopped very fine
    3 lb (1½ kilos) peeled tomatoes
    6 tablespoonsful raw sugar
    3 tablespoonsful sea salt
    25 fl oz (710ml) cider vinegar

Boil gently for an hour, stirring frequently. Pour into warm jars. Seal.

Cole Slaw Sauce (for use with white raw shredded cabbage).

Here are two recipes for this delicious sauce, the first more suitable for general use, the second for a special occasion.

Standard

Dissolve 2 oz (50g) butter over a low heat, add 1 tablespoonful flour (81 per cent wholemeal). Slowly add 4 fl oz (100ml) water, stirring all the time, to make a cream. Cook until smooth and quite thick. Beat 2 eggs, 2 tablespoonsful raw sugar, 1 teaspoonful mustard powder and a pinch of sea salt in a bowl. Then pour over hot mixture, stirring constantly. Return the lot to the *low* heat. As soon as it thickens, take off heat. Add 4 fl oz (100ml) cider vinegar. Cool before using.

Special

    6 egg yolks
    1 tablespoonful butter
    1 teaspoonful mustard powder
    2 tablespoonsful raw sugar (light coloured)
    8 fl oz (225ml) cider vinegar
    juice of one lemon
    5 fl oz (150ml) double cream, whipped

Beat the eggs over water (see *Hollandaise* recipe). When they lighten in colour add everything except lemon juice and cream. Beat over heat until thick, add lemon juice and beat again. When cold stir in the cream.

Mint Sauces
Take a large enough bunch of mint, wash clean, take off the leaves, chop fine (we use a cheap gadget of French origin). Add, for four people, one teaspoonful raw sugar, cover with cider vinegar. Leave for at least half-an-hour before using.

We like also mint jelly. To do that add 1 tablespoonful gelatine crystals to 4 fl oz (100ml) hot cider vinegar. When dissolved, add 4 fl oz (100ml) cold cider vinegar together with raw sugar and mint as above.

Poivrade Sauce (hot, for meats and vegetarian roasts)

    1 large chopped onion
    2 grated carrots
    3 tablespoonsful chopped parsley
    2 tablespoonsful corn oil
    ½ bay leaf
    pinch thyme

Cook together for five minutes or so.
    Add: 5 fl oz (150ml) red wine
    3 tablespoonsful cider vinegar.
Cook until reduced to half.
    Add: 12 fl oz (350ml) thick brown gravy. Cook for half-an-hour. Strain into clean saucepan with a pinch of ground cloves and 2 teaspoonsful freshly ground black pepper. Stir well and cook gently for five minutes more.

Sorrel Sauce
A traditional accompaniment to vegetables. This

recipe is seventeenth-century.

Crush about 3 oz (75g) of chopped sorrel with the flesh of two peeled eating apples. Beat in a teaspoonful of raw sugar and a tablespoonful of cider vinegar. No need to cook this one!

Sweet and Sour Sauce (Beloved of the Chinese and good with many fried things and undercooked vegetables.)

    8 tablespoonsful cider vinegar
    8 tablespoonsful honey
    1 small green pepper (sweet) chopped fine
    1 tablespoonful chopped almonds

Mix and heat gently before serving. You can also add a clove of crushed garlic. If you prefer a milder sweet and sour sauce, add up to half-a-pint of stock to taste.

Worcestershire Sauce
Most recipes for this famous sauce contain a lot of anchovies, which are not to every taste. Here is a well-tried method, too extravagant for the commercial producer. A cheap sherry, preferably dry, is good enough.

    2 teaspoonsful pimento
    1 teaspoonful clove
    1 teaspoonful black pepper
    1 teaspoonful ginger
    1 teaspoonful chilli powder
    1 oz (25g) curry powder
    2 oz (50g) mustard
    2 oz (50g) bruised shallots
    2 oz (50g) sea salt
    8 oz (225g) raw sugar (dark)
    4 oz (100g) tamarinds
    1 pint (575ml) sherry
    2 pints (1 litre) cider vinegar
    a touch of caramel to colour

Use whole spices where available. Bruise them by roughly pounding. Simmer everything, except the sherry, together for an hour. Top up with more cider vinegar if any has been lost by evaporation. Add the sherry and any colour needed (caramel). Leave for a week. Coarsely strain and bottle.

CHUTNEY, PICKLES AND MUSTARDS

You can substitute cider vinegar for ordinary vinegar in any recipe, but here are some tested and occasionally unusual ways of making these excellent accompaniments.

Apple Chutney (An old Devon recipe)

    40 fl oz (1 litre) cider vinegar
    2 lb (1 kilo) apples (cored and peeled)
    1 lb (450g) raw sugar
    1 lb (450g) raisins (seedless)
    2 teaspoonsful sea salt
    1 lb (450g) onions
    1 oz (25g) mustard powder
    1 teaspoonful cayenne pepper

Chop all ingredients coarsely. Boil until tender, about one hour. Pour into hot jars. Seal.

Apple and Blackberry Chutney (another Devon treat)

    1½ lb (675g) apples (cored and peeled)
    1½ lb (675g) blackberries
    10 fl oz (275ml) cider vinegar
    ½ lb (225g) raw sugar
    1 teaspoonful sea salt
    4 oz (100g) raisins (seedless)
    4 oz (100g) sultanas
    2 cloves crushed garlic *or*
    3 small chopped onions
    1 teaspoonful ground ginger

Crush the blackberries in the pan with the vinegar. Simmer for twenty minutes and rub through a coarse sieve (I use a colander). Add the other ingredients. Cook gently until thick, this takes about forty minutes. Pour into hot jars and seal.

Green Tomato Chutney

This recipe was devised by Martlet. None of my garden-grown tomatoes ripened one year so we tried this recipe and found it very good.

    4 lb (2 kilos) green tomatoes
    1½ lb (675g) onions
    1½ lb (675g.) apples (after peeling and coring)
    1 lb (450g) sultanas
    2 lb (1 kilo) raw sugar
    2 oz (50g) mustard powder
    4 oz (100g) sea salt
    1 oz (25g) ground ginger
    1 oz (25g) crushed garlic
    1 teaspoonful cayenne pepper
    juice of 2 lemons
    2½ pints (1½ litres) cider vinegar

Slice the tomatoes, apples and onions thinly. Mix well with the other ingredients. Simmer for 2 hours or until well cooked and thick

Bengal Apple Chutney

This is highly spiced and a first-rate accompaniment to curries and savouries.

    3 pints (1¾ litres) cider vinegar
    1 lb (450g) raw sugar
    2 oz (50g) mustard seed
    8 oz (225g) raisins (seedless)
    2 oz (50g) garlic
    8 oz (225g) onions
    7 lb (3 kilos) cooking apples
    2 tablespoonsful sea salt

½ oz (15g) chilli powder
1 teaspoonful cumin powder (if available)
2 oz (50g) fresh ginger *or*
4 teaspoonsful powdered ginger

Scrape the ginger, but mind the eyes whilst you do it! Mince it with the onions and garlic. Core, slice and peel the apples. Simmer the apples with the cider vinegar and raw sugar until the apples are quite soft. Add everything else and simmer for another twenty minutes, stirring frequently. Bottle.

Tomato Ketchup
Ketchup is a modern word for thin chutney. In about 1690 it was called *catchup*. In the 1730s the name became *catsup*, which is often still used in America. Only in the last century was ketchup made commonly with tomatoes. Before then, walnuts and mushrooms were the usual basis.

3 lb (1½ kilos) tomatoes
2 oz (50g) sea salt
1 pint (575ml) cider vinegar
2 oz (50g) raw sugar
2 teaspoonsful mustard powder
1 teaspoonful pepper

Peel the tomatoes by plunging them first into boiling water for a second. Chop them coarsely, sprinkle with the sea salt and allow to stand for at least 3 hours. Boil with the other ingredients for half an hour, stirring frequently until thick and smooth. Fill into clean bottles whilst still hot. Keep for a few days before using.

Hot Peach Chutney
This is best made with slightly unripe peaches. If you do not want it hot, replace the chilli and

ginger by a teaspoon of mustard powder and ¼ teaspoonful of pepper.

    2 lb (1 kilo) peaches
    1 lb (450g) raw sugar
    1 pint (575ml) cider vinegar
    8 oz (225g) sultanas
    1 oz (25g) chilli powder
    1 teaspoonful ginger powder

Skin the peaches. Halve them and remove the stones. Bring half the cider vinegar to the boil with the raw sugar. Lower the halved peaches into the liquid. Simmer until they are soft. Add all the remaining ingredients. Simmer until thick. Bottle. This is best matured for a few weeks to bring out the flavour. The recipe is worth trying with plums. These do not need peeling.

Pickled Onions

In olden times you used a silver knife for peeling the onions as steel discolours the flesh. Today stainless steel is fine. We like our onions crisp. If you prefer yours softer then cook them for 5-7 minutes in the spiced vinegar before bottling

After you have peeled the onions, cover them with water to which has been added 3 ounces (75g) sea salt for every pint (575ml). As the onions like to float, I put a plate on top to keep them down. Leave the onions for at least twenty-four hours — forty-eight hours or longer does no harm — before thoroughly draining them.

Spiced Vinegar is best made at the same time as you brine the onions. You can buy ready mixed pickling spice which is very good, but if you prefer to make your own use, to every quart (litre) of vinegar: ¼ ounce (7½g) allspice, ¼ ounce (7½g) blade mace, ½

CIDER VINEGAR IN THE KITCHEN 87

ounce (7½g) cinnamon sticks, 20 peppercorns and, if liked, ¼ oz (7½g) root ginger in the piece, plus four or five whole dried red chillies.

You can either tie the spices in a bag of muslin (in which case add ¼ oz (7½g) cloves) or you can, as we do, bottle the spices with the onions. The first way looks best. We prefer the flavour the second way. In either case, simmer the spices in the vinegar for an hour, with the lid on a stainless steel saucepan, and leave to cool and mature until the onions are ready for bottling. Pack the dry onions carefully into sterile jars (leaving the empty jars for an hour in the oven on gas mark 1 or electric 275°F (140°C) and allow to cool). Pour on the spiced vinegar and store in a cool place.

This method works also with cauliflower, green tomatoes and cucumbers.

Piccalilli

    3 lb (1½ kilos) green tomatoes
    ½ lb (225g) cabbage
    1 lb (450g) cauliflower florets
    1 large cucumber
    4 medium sized onions *plus*
        20 pickling onions if available
    2 tablespoonsful sea salt
    2 pints (1 litre) cider vinegar
    1 lb (450g) raw sugar
    3 teaspoonsful turmeric
    4 oz (100g) mustard powder
    1 teaspoonful black pepper
    2 oz (50g) tapioca starch or
        if not available, cornflour

Mix the tapioca powder or cornflour in a little cider vinegar then simmer the rest of the ingredients for fifteen minutes. Turn off the heat, add the cider vinegar/tapioca or starch mixture and allow to cool. Chop all the vegetables and place in layers in basins with layers of sea salt between. Let this stay overnight. Drain off the liquid completely. Mix the sauce and the vegetables thoroughly. Put into sterile jars, seal carefully. Ready for use in two weeks.

Pickled Crab Apples

This recipe works with any small sour apple, but it is a good way of using crab apples:

    5 lb (2¼ kilos) crab apples
    1¾ pints (1 litre) cider vinegar
    2 lb (1 kilo) raw sugar
    pickling spices in a bag (see pages 86, 87)

Stir the sugar into the cider vinegar, drop in the spice bag, and bring to the boil in a container that is not aluminium. Simmer gently for twenty minutes, removing any scum that forms on the surface.

Trim the ends of the apples, wash carefully and add to the simmering mixture. Continue cooking until the apples begin to soften. Pack them into jars without any liquid which then has to be reduced until it becomes syrupy. Pour over the apples whilst still hot and then seal securely.

Pickled Red Cabbage

For this wonderful preparation which is a splendid accompaniment to many savoury dishes both hot and cold you will need:

    4 lb (2 kilos) red cabbage
    5 oz (350g) sea salt
    10 shredded bay leaves
    2 tablespoonsful black peppercorns
    2 oz (60g) sliced fresh ginger root
    1 oz (25g) allspice
    cider vinegar as necessary

Prepare cabbages as in previous recipe. Spread them out into flat non-metallic dishes, sprinkle with sea-salt, then lightly cover with a cloth or kitchen paper. Let it stand for twenty-four hours.

Drain the cabbage through a large sieve, cover again and leave for a further day with the occasional shake. Sprinkle the spice mixture all over the cabbage so that it is well mixed but not bruised. Gently put the mixture into jars without pressing down. Leave some room above the top of the cabbage. Cover with cider vinegar which needs to be quite cold.

It is important to be sure that the jars used are very clean indeed and that, after filling, you seal down very firmly so that no air can get in. The pickle is ready to eat within a month and is well worth waiting for.

Pickled Eggs
Cider vinegar has the special property of preventing discolouration of the eggs. All you have to do is to gently boil the eggs for twenty minutes, shell them while still quite hot and drop them straight into cider vinegar in a storage jar.

Pickled Sausages
Lovely for picnics, especially if you can obtain your sausages from a reliable butcher who avoids extenders, binders, emulsifiers and the like.

Deep fry the sausages in corn oil until well-done. Drop them straight into cider vinegar. They will keep for months in a cool place.

Rollmops
Soak herring fillets in brine, just as for pickled onions, with 3 ounces (75g) sea salt to each pint

(575ml) of water, but with the addition of 2 tablespoonsful of cider vinegar to each pint (575ml). Leave them for four hours in a cool place. Then replace the brine with cider vinegar with 1 ounce (25g) sea salt per pint (575ml), and leave for a further twelve hours. Finally wrap each fillet round some shredded onion and fasten the tail with a cocktail stick. Put in fresh cider vinegar with some herbs or spices, especially paprika and bay leaves, if you like. They will keep for four weeks or much longer in the fridge.

Mackerel in Vinegar

Fillet the fish. Dry them by dredging with flour. Fry in corn oil until golden. Leave to cool. Put a layer of the fish into a bowl, sprinkle with sea salt and raw sugar then another layer of fish and so on until all is used. Slice an onion thickly, put this over the top layer, sprinkle with pepper. Cover with cider vinegar. Leave in a cool place for two or three days. Taste the vinegar adding more raw sugar if required. This keeps for weeks in a cool place.

English Mustard

Instead of mixing powdered mustard with water, use cider vinegar. Allow the mixture to stand for about half-an-hour to develop the flavour. Mustard tastes better and keeps longer this way.

German Mustard

Take 2 ounces (50g) mustard powder with 1 ounce (25g) cornflour or tapioca flour. Mix in a large pinch each of ginger powder, ground cloves, ground carraway seeds, a teaspoonful of sea salt and two of raw sugar. Make the lot into a fairly thick mustard by gently cooking it with half a pint (225ml) of cider vinegar. Allow to cool and store in small sealed pots.

DRINKS

There are some old ways of using cider vinegar as an essential ingredient for a refreshing summer drink.

Cowslip Cider Vinegar

Collect a quarter of a pound (100g) of cowslip 'pips', as the flowers are called, pull them from the stalks, cover with a pint (575ml) of cider vinegar and allow to marinade for three days. Strain the liquor through a fine sieve or some muslin into a stainless steel or enamelled saucepan. Add 1 lb (450g) of raw sugar and stir until dissolved. Put the lid on and stand the pan in a larger pan of boiling water. Cook like this for an hour, topping up the water, as necessary. Bottle when cold. It is better if you add a wineglass of brandy to each pint (575ml)! Dilute with soda or ice cold water, as required.

Elderflower Sparkling Wine

You will need 2 heads elderflowers in full bloom, 1 lemon, 2 tablespoonsful cider vinegar, 1 gallon cold water and 1½ lb (675g) raw sugar.

Squeeze the lemon and put with the quartered peel into a non-metal container. Add the other ingredients and leave for twenty-four hours. Strain and pour into clean, screw-top bottles. Keep for at least two weeks before using.

Fruit Cider Vinegars

Many people in olden times thought a drink of a diluted fruit cider vinegar was a good winter health promoter. You may like to try the idea. You can use any soft fruit, raspberries and blackcurrants being especially nice. You can use up the small or squashed fruits very well this way. Use one pint (575ml) of cider vinegar to each pound (450g) of fruit. Mix the cider vinegar and fruit together and stir them from time to time for about five days. Strain the liquid, pressing out as much as possible from the fruit pulp. Add half-a-pound (225g),or more to taste, of light raw sugar to each pint (575ml). Boil for ten minutes and fill into warmed bottles, whilst still hot.

You can use these vinegars as interesting varieties for dressings but they are excellent as a drink, when you may wish to add extra sugar.

SOME OTHER IDEAS
Cheese Softening
In 1577, a certain B. Goodge wrote these words, 'Hard cheese wrapped in cloutes wet in cyder vinegar returnes to a softness.'

Stopping Potatoes Browning
Add a good splash of cider vinegar to the water into which you slice potatoes. When you have finished you can dry them, prior to frying, with far less chance of their going brown.

Steaming Vegetables
When you cook vegetables by the healthy method of steaming them (there is less vitamin and mineral loss this way), add 2 teaspoonsful of cider vinegar to the water you use. This helps the vegetables keep their colour without the vitamin C depleting effect that comes from using bicarbonate of soda.

Poached Eggs

I do not care for those moulded eggs which come from bought egg poachers. They seem to lack interest and excitement. I put a saucepan of water on to boil, add two teaspoonsful of cider vinegar and wait until it is simmering gently.

Meanwhile I have cracked one or two eggs into a small container or cup which is less than half the width of the pan.

With a wooden spoon I briskly stir the bubbling liquid. When it is going smoothly, I gently pour the eggs into the vortex of the little whirlpool that has been created. The whites coagulate nicely and in two minutes I am ready to serve the poached eggs upon wholemeal toast.

Furniture Polish

This is not a joke! Nor have I substituted cider vinegar in a recipe usually using the ordinary type. The formula, as it stands, is the recommendation of the United States Bureau of Standards.

Cider vinegar	12½ pounds (5¾ kilos)
Petroleum spirits	22¼ pounds (10 kilos)
Turpentine	13½ pounds (6 kilos)
Denatured alcohol	2¼ pounds (1 kilo)
Boiled linseed oil	10 pounds (4½ kilos)
Raw linseed oil	12 pounds (5½ kilos)

These quantities produce 10 gallons (45 litres) of polish which should *not* be stored in metal containers because these may be corroded by the cider vinegar. You can use ounces instead of pounds for a smaller quantity of this very economical and good quality polish.

SAVOURY DISHES

My family loves the added aroma and softness cider vinegar gives to so many dishes. Here are a few you may like trying – our tastes embrace many ways of eating so keep on tasting until the dish suits you. I am sure there are many folk tales in cookery, one of them is flaming a dish in brandy. This expensive waste can be replaced by a quarter of the brandy, not flamed, added just before you serve. Sometimes a dish of angostura bitters does instead, this is especially good in soups. To start with a real scorcher:

Vindaloo Chicken
You require:

    1 3lb (1½ kilo) chicken
    1 teaspoonful mustard powder
    2 teaspoonsful chilli powder
    2 teaspoonsful cumin powder
    6 cloves
    6 cloves of garlic (unless you are frightened)
    2 teaspoonsful turmeric (sold in Indian shops)
    1 teaspoonful ginger
    1 stick cinnamon
    1 tablespoonful raw sugar
    2 tablespoonsful sea salt
    3 tablespoonsful corn oil
    3 tablespoonsful cider vinegar
    2 large onions

Take all the ingredients except the chicken, onion and oil, mix them to a pulp, crushing the garlic and cloves. Cut up the chicken, cover all parts with the mixture. Leave for at least five hours, a day is better, in a cool place. Fry the onion in corn oil. Add the chicken and spices. Cook in a closed saucepan until the chicken is cooked through. I like an extra sprinkle of cumin just before serving.

Vindaloo Vegetables
The foregoing recipe can also be used with certain vegetables, either a mixture or, more successfully, courgettes, aubergines, mushrooms and sweet peppers.

Barbecued Spare Ribs of Pork
Cheap and lovely. If you do not have a barbecue, use a medium grill to finish off. The recipe will do for four pounds (2 kilos) of spare ribs. Take:

    4 tablespoonsful sherry
    1¼ pint (725ml) white stock (or a good cube)
    1 tablespoonful honey
    2 tablespoonsful cider vinegar
    1 tablespoonful soya sauce
    1 tablespoonful raw sugar
    1 teaspoonful ginger powder
    2 cloves crushed garlic

Mix all the ingredients. Cut up the spare ribs, marinade for twenty-four hours in a cool place. Take out the ribs and roast in a pan at 350°F (180°C) or Gas Mark 5. Drain off fat, finish on barbecue or under grill, basting with marinade, until crisp.

Rice Salad
You can use mushrooms or prawns instead of the anchovy fillets, if you prefer. Take:

    ½ lb (225g) rice (basmati is best;
        patna almost as good)
    2 oz (50g) tin anchovy fillets
    4 oz (100g) olives (stoned: black are best)
    3 tablespoonsful corn oil
    1 tablespoonful cider vinegar, sea salt, pepper
    1 sliced tomato
    1 cupful cooked green peas

Cook the rice in lots of boiling, sea salted water. After ten minutes fish out a grain and test it for softness with your finger nails. Do this again each minute until the rice has softened moderately. Drain the rice through a sieve, wash with cold running water. Drain completely, put in a basin until cold. Add the other ingredients having mixed the oil, cider vinegar, pepper and sea salt. Stir gently until completely mixed. Decorate with a sliced green pepper or tomato.

Shashlik

Take and cut into large cubes enough lean, tender lamb for your needs. Put the lamb to marinade for about half a day in enough cider vinegar to cover, with lots of raw onion rings.

Skewer the cubes. You can, if you wish, alternate the lamb with green peppers, bacon and sliced tomatoes. Brush with corn oil and grill on a hot flame until done. Serve with the onion rings from the cider vinegar, sprinkle with cumin seed and perhaps a little salt and paprika.

Pork Chops in Tomato

6 pork chops
1 cupful cider vinegar
1 cupful stock (or beef stock cube)
1 tablespoonful corn oil
4 tablespoonsful tomato paste

Trim fat from chops and seal quickly in hot corn oil. Pour off any fat in the pan, add the cider vinegar. Cover pan and simmer, turning chops from time to time. When the cider vinegar has greatly reduced, add the other ingredients and cook for half-an-hour more. If the sauce is too thick, add more water.

Mexican Hot Pot
Brown 1 lb (450g) diced stewing steak with 2 large, sliced onions. Add 1 teaspoonful chilli powder, 1 teaspoonful sea salt, 1 tablespoonful cider vinegar, 1 cupful water or stock. Cook gently in the oven for two hours. If you like, add haricot beans before cooking, in which case add extra water.

Partridge in Chocolate
An exotic and delicious Spanish dish. Chicken will do as an alternative. You will need:

    1 partridge
    1 cupful boiling water
    3 tablespoonsful cider vinegar
    1 tablespoonful parsley
    3 cloves garlic
    corn oil
    2 tablespoonsful grated plain chocolate
    1 tablespoonful wholemeal breadcrumbs

Brown the bird in a casserole with the hot oil. Add the garlic, parsley and chopped onion and brown them lightly. Then put in the cider vinegar and boiling water. Stew gently in the oven until cooked then increase heat, add the chocolate and breadcrumbs and boil for a few minutes before serving.

Almond and Garlic Soup with Grapes
Another Spanish recipe, from Malaga where the grapes are sweet. There they use freshly shelled almonds dried slightly in the oven and then .powdered. We use the less beautiful shop-bought ground almonds, but the soup is an interesting summer starter.

Z

2 tablespoonsful ground almonds
6 cloves garlic
2 tablespoonsful corn oil
1 pint (575ml) water
1½ tablespoonsful cider vinegar
8 ice cubes
2 teaspoonsful sea salt
1 lb (450g) skinned, seeded grapes
½ cupful wholemeal breadcrumbs

Pound together with garlic; almonds, salt and oil until smooth. Add the cider vinegar, grapes, water and ice cubes. Leave one hour in a cold place before serving.

Gazpacho Soup
This most famous Spanish cold soup comes from Andalusia. You can either pound the solid ingredients together, apart from the cucumber, then add the oil drop by drop until it becomes thick when you stir in the cider vinegar and add the cucumber; or you can save trouble by using a blender to do your initial blend, adding the oil whilst still blending. If it is too thick, add some water. Add the ice. Chill before serving and garnish with chopped parsley or chives. You need:

5 tomatoes
4 cloves garlic
½ cupful cider vinegar
1 chopped onion
sea salt and pepper
½ cucumber, finely chopped
1 cupful wholemeal breadcrumbs
1 sweet red pepper, chopped
8 ice cubes

Cold Potatoes
An excellent accompaniment for savouries of all sorts.

1¼ lb (675g) small new potatoes (unpeeled)
2 oz (50g) streaky bacon
2 tablespoonsful cider vinegar
2 tablespoonsful chopped chives or onion

Cut the potatoes into pieces and sprinkle with the chives or onion. Sprinkle with sea salt and pepper. Dice the fat bacon and cook it in its own fat until crisp. Add the vinegar very carefully because it foams. Pour over the potatoes and serve when cold.

Boiled Salmon

I find that this way does just as well for lobster which takes twenty minutes in the boiling liquor. Salmon takes about thirty minutes, then you let it cool, in the fridge, in the juice, This·makes the salmon very moist and it will keep for a day or so if needed.

Slice 2 onions, 2 carrots and a leek, if you have it, into ¼ pint (150ml) of cider vinegar, plus half-a-pint of white wine, or water will do. Add 3 pints (1¾ litres) of water, a large handful of parsley with about a third as much thyme and two bay leaves. Grind in some black pepper. Bring to the boil and simmer gently for an hour. Put in the salmon and simmer until done. It is often easier to lower and raise the fish on a piece of muslin.

Pickled Herring – Swedish Style
You will need:

2 small or 1 large salt herring
1 large sliced onion
3 tablespoonsful raw sugar
1 cupful cider vinegar
¼ cupful water
3 bay leaves
½ teaspoonful white pepper

Soak the herrings in cold water overnight. Dry them and then remove the skin and bones. Slice them into equal sized narrow pieces, arrange them in a dish. Mix all the other ingredients together and pour them over the fish. Cover and leave in a refrigerator for at least eight hours for the flavours to blend.

Spanish Grilled Mushrooms

Put the required number of mushrooms, which have been carefully washed, in a dish and then sprinkle liberally with olive or corn oil and season with sea salt and freshly ground black pepper. Allow the mushrooms to marinade in this mixture for several hours giving an occasional gentle stir.

Take out the mushrooms, grill them under a hot grill (broil in the United States) until they are just cooked. Transfer them to a warm serving dish. Fry two or three chopped cloves of garlic and some parsley in the marinading mixture, some chives can also be added with advantage, stir in one tablespoonful cider vinegar, pour the sauce over the mushrooms and serve at once.

Cacik (Turkish Cucumber Soup)

You need for this very nice cold soup (which might have been invented by a health food cook):

    1 peeled halved and seeded cucumber
    3 x 5 oz (150g) cartons plain yogurt
    2 teaspoonsful cider vinegar
    1 small teaspoonful corn oil
    milk
    2 teaspoonsful chopped mint

Grate the cucumber and blend it with the yogurt (or put them in a liquidizer). Season to taste, add the oil and cider vinegar. Mix well, then thin to the required consistency with cold milk.

Chill well and just before serving put into cold bowls and sprinkle with the chopped mint.

CHAPTER SIX

CIDER VINEGAR IN THE TREATMENT OF ANIMALS

As I have implied, this section is the key to the whole cider vinegar system of treatment. The allergy specialist, Dr Erik Anderson, who had many reports of the effective use of cider vinegar, honey and beeswax among his patients, said that it has become a rule of thumb in tests which include placebos (that is, treatments using an ingredient which the patient believes is the one that will work, whereas an inert alternative is used instead) that up to a third of the placebo group frequently feels an improvement.

What we humans experience when we are ill is often reduced, aggravated or maybe even caused by our mental processes. I have no reason to believe that cows, pigs, sheep and horses fall into this psychologically motivated category. Yet cider vinegar works very regularly in some common animal complaints. It is used regularly by farmers who certainly cannot afford to waste money on an outside chance of improvement.

This gives me good reason to believe that the remarkable results observed from the use of cider vinegar in man are not just faith healing but are a real and positive contribution to sound health.

Many theories have been proposed as to why

cider vinegar works and it may be that there is not one answer but several. More research is required and is, I know, being undertaken in certain areas of study, such as asthma. A most interesting and exciting recent observation was that one of the causative organisms of mastitis in the cow, *Streptococcus mammitis*, when grown in the laboratory, is killed by the application of a small amount of cider vinegar. In response to my enquiries, the chemist told me that neither ordinary vinegar of the same acidity nor cider itself had this effect. Here then is a piece of concrete evidence that there is something very special about cider vinegar. In this connexion, the suggestion has been made that the natural balance of phenols and tannins in the acetic cider vinegar is not all that different from the basic chemical materials from which scientists produce bacteria-destroying drugs. The thought this raises is the profound idea that through the use of cider vinegar you enable the body to produce within itself valuable substances for its own protection. It will take many years to test the truth of this proposition, but it is a most provoking suggestion. The chemist in question, Mr Loates of Whiteways, gave me his view on cyder vinegar and the farmer.

CYDER VINEGAR AND THE FARMER
In these days of antibiotics and synthetic drugs for treatment of both human and animal ailments, the use of natural remedies has been neglected.

For many years the curative and beneficial properties of country remedies were well known and well used, and undoubtedly they had effects which could not be ignored. The great increase in the use of Whiteways Cyder Vinegar by stockmen for treating cattle and pigs during the past few years has shown that these natural remedies do work and are well worth trying.

In primitive areas of France and other parts of Europe, the use of Cyder Vinegar remains a traditional treatment for many cattle ailments. Cattle, sheep, deer and other related animals have a specialized digestive process, and it is upon the proper and efficient functioning of this that the health and condition of the animal depends.

McAnally and Phillipson have dealt with this matter extensively and it might well be of interest to state the basic principles involved. The animals nourish themselves upon grass and similar plant life whose chief contribution is in the form of fibrous carbohydrate cellulose. The indigestible nature of such plant material makes it necessary for large quantities of food to be taken in by the animal in order that its body may obtain sufficient digestible material for its needs.

The digestion of cellulose is accomplished, not by the secretions from the glands of the animal, but by bacteria which inhabit the alimentary canal and which break down the complex carbohydrates into readily assimilable · products. The enlarged and elaborated portions of the canal of such animals enable the passage of the ingested material to be delayed at optimum conditions of temperature, moisture and acidity for the action of the bacteria to accomplish the digestive process.

The ruminants have developed for this purpose a stomach divided into four areas, and normally the solid food is swallowed as grazed into the rumen where it may be retained for up to several days. It is subjected to a constant churning and mixing caused by muscular contractions after which it is brought back into the mouth and thoroughly chewed before passing again to the rumen where the finer particles pass on through the omasum to the abomasum, where further digestion takes place.

The chief bacterial process achieved in the rumen is the breakdown of cellulose and carbohydrates to simple organic acids and gasses. The chief of these is acetic acid which is absorbed into the blood-stream, thus providing a source of energy directly from the cellulose. Protein and amino acids are synthesized and stored in the bacteria themselves which pass on and undergo further digestion in the intestine. Vitamins can also be synthesized by the bacteria of the rumen and contribute essentially to the well-being of the animal.

It has been suggested that the formation of acetic acid in the rumen promotes cudding, which ensures the proper working of the digestive system, and the addition of small quantities of Cyder Vinegar to the feed provides the necessary acidity to ensure this. Loss of appetite and cessation of cudding indicates that the rumen has ceased or slowed down its action, due perhaps to badly balanced rations or too finely ground foods. The composition of concentrates can encourage the production of substances in the rumen which retard the normal bacterial action and Cyder Vinegar is able to replace the naturally formed acid and so assist the normal digestive process.

Acetonaemia is a condition of accumulation of fat in the liver which results in certain breakdown products of the fat – ketones – being released into the blood-stream. One of these, acetone, creates the sweet smell noticed in the cow's breath and milk that is characteristic of the condition.

Its cause is said to be an insufficiency of the right sort of substances which prevent the liver from oxidizing the fat in the normal way. These substances consist essentially of sugars broken down from the cellulose in the rumen. It appears to be associated with lack of adequate roughage, and high-yielders fed with a below minimum ration of roughage, to enable them to consume a full concentrate ration, are often prone to digestive troubles and acetonaemia.

Some stockmen add sugar or molasses to the feed to control this condition, but the production of natural sugars by feeding a good ration of hay, at least 6 lb per day for high yielders, with an acidified (Cyder Vinegar) concentrate, is likely to be more effective.

The generally recommended dose is 2 fl oz (50ml) of Cyder Vinegar twice a day, poured over the feed. Larger doses are recommended in acute cases, up to 4 fl oz (100ml) twice a day, which can do no harm.

Dr D.C. Jarvis was the first to systematically investigate the effects of cider vinegar on large groups of cattle. He considered that it helped to maintain a correct balance between the acids and alkalis in the animal's body chemistry. He found this to be of crucial importance in building up resistance to many common farm-yard illnesses. At first he thought that the potassium content was the effective factor, so he carried out experiments which showed that the cider vinegar had a good effect not obtained from the use of potassium alone. I shall deal with some of the most successful uses of cider vinegar in animal treatment. Although the animals are dealt with individually, the experience of one is often applicable to another. It is therefore worth looking for any condition not specifically considered in the section devoted to other animals.

FOR CATTLE

Unquestionably the greatest agricultural use for cider vinegar is in the treatment and prevention of common ailments amongst cattle and for improving general condition, milk yield and fertility.

The usual dose for adult animals is about four fluid ounces (100ml) per day which may be given as just over two tablespoonsful, twice a day.

If the animal is suffering from poor appetite, the cider vinegar can be used as a drench with equal quantities of warm water. A drench – for the non-farmer – is a liquid given directly into the mouth of the animal from a bottle which has usually a rubber or plastic end. This can be given twice a day until the appetite is restored when the mixture can be poured over the concentrated rations.

Younger or smaller animals require proportionately less. Heifers at bulling age need two fluid ounces (50ml) once a day, weaned calves one fluid ounce (25ml) a day and new-born calves two teaspoonsful each day.

LET THE FACTS SPEAK FOR THEMSELVES

Mr John Waring, who has a herd of pedigree Friesians at Kilnwick Percy in Yorkshire, wrote to Whiteways about his experience with cider vinegar and his record-breaking cow *Winton Pel Eva II*. Here is his letter in full:

Three years ago the above cow appeared on television being one of the few cows ever to produce 100 tons of milk. An elderly lady who had seen the programme wrote to me. Apparently she had been connected with Jersey cattle in New Zealand for some fifty years. She said I would know what would take my cow as indeed we all know that all cows from about 12 years start to get arthritis and it is the one immobility for which they have to be destroyed. In fact they get down and cannot get up. It was purely through an accident that they found a cure for this, or indeed a prevention.

A number of cider barrels had been left to steep for several weeks and the residue was eventually poured through the fence into a field. The jersey cows ate the grass and some of the soil. After this they prepared something similar and this they found prevented arthritis.

From that day on we started to feed $2\frac{1}{2}$ pints of cider vinegar per week to the above cow. She is now sixteen years old with no sign of arthritis whatsoever. She is in calf again with her thirteenth calf and never looked fitter. She has now produced 138 tons of milk. The World Record, held by an American Holstein, is 145.6 tons. My cow is now well within striking distance and, all being well, this time next year she will have done it.

Another point of interest, after being on cider vinegar she never had milk fever again, and at all previous calvings we nearly lost her. My vet said on the first occasion it was a coincidence but after the next two calvings has never mentioned it again.

We get a lot of visitors to see the cow and numerous people with old valuable cows are going on to it, as indeed a lot of elderly people themselves are taking it. I wonder if you have noticed any significant increase in sales.

I brought this up at the National Cattle Breeders

Club at Cambridge last week and this stimulated a lot of interest but, as there were a lot of professors and doctors etc. in the veterinary world present, they tried to play it cool. But I am certain it really captured the interest of the Cattle Breeders and they are going to try it.

I had fifty Canadians here this summer and they said arthritis took most of their old cows at about fourteen years. The mother of my cow is buried in the orchard here. She went down with arthritis at 16½ but apart from that was perfectly healthy and would have lived several years more.

Yours sincerely,
John Waring

TREATMENT OF MASTITIS

Both *Streptococcal* and *Staphylococcal mastitis* seem to be improved by cider vinegar although, as pointed out earlier in this section, the successful laboratory tests have been upon the more resistant *Streptococcus mammitis* not upon the antibiotic-sensitive *Staphylococcus agalactiae*.

The trouble with antibiotic treatment, apart from the cost, is the effect upon the milk because of the unacceptable residue of antibiotic formed therein.

Treatment with cider vinegar by means of a daily ration or drench of up to eight fluid ounces (225ml) a day for three days, then half as much, usually produces clear, clot-free milk within seven days. A regular daily dose prevents further attacks. The milk can be sent to the dairy as soon as it is normal. Milk is never tainted nor harmed in any way from the use of cider vinegar.

When the shape or texture of a quarter of the udder is badly affected it may take up to eight weeks to return to normal. However it has recently been reported that an injection of 5ml of cider vinegar directly into the infected quarter will reduce nodules and clear up infections almost immediately. Prevention and early treatment is best.

The treatment usually seems to work even when the infection is resistant to antibiotics. Some case histories illustrate this point.

Farmer W.J.E. of Haverfordwest learnt his skills from a cowman who came from the Cambridge University Farm who had always used cider vinegar for mastitis. He completely cured two of his cows and quite a few of his neighbour's which were still seriously ill even after massive doses of antibiotics from the veterinary surgeon.

Farmer J.C.O. of Axminster wrote that he had used it on his cattle for years, two tablespoonsful twice a day on their nuts. Before doing this they had terrible mastitis and warble fly.

Farmer R.J.I.W. who has a herd of Ayrshires in Cheshire used the Milk Marketing Board cell-count test to find sub-clinical mastitis. He had been using cider vinegar successfully for some time for clinical mastitis but was worried to find from the tests that a high incidence of invisible mastitis affected the untreated part of the herd. He then treated them all with cider vinegar. The first result was that many of the sub-clinical cases became clinical, but then all cleared up. He thought this might be a step in the elimination of the infection.

Farmer K.J.R. of the Isle of Wight after using cider vinegar on his forty-five Ayrshires for two years was able to say that mastitis had become a rare occurrence.

In the magazine *Dairy Farmer* for December 1967, Mike Walsh wrote how he had, like other readers, successfully used cider vinegar for mastitis but found his results to be not always consistent. He says it is useful in restoring a cow's appetite and also not expensive.

He goes on to mention that an eggcupful every morning will soon have any dairy farmer with rheumatism skipping around like a new-born lamb. And if the dairymaid has a slimming problem she will find it very useful although she will have to watch out for the rejuvenated dairy farmer!

A supplier of cider vinegar to Cumberland farmers relates how after a trial lasting just three weeks he thought cider vinegar wonderful stuff because it had completely cleared up a persistent mastitis problem. Furthermore, the cows had a bloom he had never ever experienced in the past.

MILK FEVER

Even when animals have a history of repeated severe attacks of milk fever, a daily four-ounce (100ml) ration of cider vinegar given from six weeks before until three weeks after calving has been completely successful in preventing the condition.

ACETONAEMIA

This condition often arises from an unbalanced diet. The liver normally, with the particular aid of certain carbohydrates, oxidizes fats. In acetonaemia it is unable to do this because of a shortage of these carbohydrates. The result is that various breakdown products of fat called *ketones* are released into the blood stream. Acetone is one of these and it causes a peculiar sweet smell of the breath and milk that is a characteristic of this disease, the other name for which is ketosis.

Glycerine and propylene glycol have both been recommended as treatments. Yet cider vinegar seems to provide an even better answer. It can be used as a preventative by giving two fluid ounces (50ml) twice daily from three to six weeks before calving until four to six weeks after. As a treatment drench with eight fluid ounces (225ml) of cider vinegar mixed with an equal quantity of warm water on the first day. On the second and successive days give 4 fl oz (100ml) diluted with an equal quantity of lukewarm water until normal appetite returns, and then add 2 fl oz (50ml) twice daily with the feed. To prevent a recurrence of the attack continue treatment for at least ten days.

Mrs E.M.C. of Calne, writing in *Farming Express*, said that her dairy herd had suffered from acetonaemia for many years. They tried both glycerine and potassium chlorate without satisfactory results even though they were expensive. She had read an article in the *Daily Express* discussing the properties of cider vinegar almost two years earlier and her family had used it ever since. She has seen her cows eat their cake within an hour of being drenched. She gives ¾-pint (425ml) or ½-pint (275ml) of cider vinegar according to animal size and there is rarely any loss of milk.

The paper's veterinary adviser thought that her results were a result of supplying the cow with the necessary organic acids which are normally present in ruminal fermentation.

IMPROVED MILK YIELDS AND CONDITION

Mrs Marrable of Marle Green, Sussex, who has a herd of twenty milking Friesians and Shorthorns, first tried small quantities of cider vinegar late in 1964. Here are her results for that and the succeeding two years:

	1965/66	1964/65	1966/67
Milk yield (lbs)	10,509	10,085	11,507
Butterfat per cent	3.59	3.61	3.56
Veterinary fees	£15	£45	£15

After the second year she wondered if other factors might have produced these changes, so she waited another year before feeling confirmed in her findings, which were published in *Farmer and Stockbreeder* in December 1967.

Mrs Marrable showed the reporter how keen the cows were on cider vinegar by tipping a small quantity on the grass when they gathered around to lick it up as eagerly as they would eat linseed cake.

This herd's fertility has improved and there have been no calving troubles or retained cleansings. The calves themselves appear extra vigorous and go to a local dealer who is prepared to pay slightly higher prices because of their sturdiness and good coats. All the cattle on the farm have the supple skin and shining coat so valued by stockmen.

Dr Jarvis found even greater increase in milk yields over a similar period, but his herd may have been in a worse condition at the start than Mrs Marrable's.

DRYING OFF IN MILK COWS

Mastitis is common at this time, and as I have

8

indicated, cider vinegar is a valuable preventative. It has been suggested that drenching can be avoided at this time if a very small ration of concentrate, even as little as six cake nuts, is placed by the cider vinegar ration in the manger. Once this becomes an established routine the cows often drink the vinegar from their manger without any concentrate in addition. The period of preventative treatment varies with the quality of hay or pasture providing maintenance, and the milking potential, from between one and three weeks. It is usual to give four fluid ounces (100ml) a day for the first week and then half as much for as long as necessary.

FERTILITY

Users universally report improved fertility from heifers and cows when they are on a four fluid-ounce (100ml) daily ration. This is particularly striking in the high first service conception rates in both bulling heifers and cows. Yet other farmers do not find a regular dose so effective as giving one pint of cider vinegar on the concentrate just before serving.

Stock bulls on a regular four-fluid-ounce (100ml) daily ration tend to maintain semen of high fertility even during slack periods. The treatment also stimulates bulls who are uninterested.

I have previously referred to the report of Mrs E.M.C. in *Farming Express*. She says that she gives cows half-a-pint (275ml) before service and had all her cows and heifers in calf during the last winter. The vet said he was not certain of the action of cider vinegar on fertility, the possible explanation being the rich mineral properties of the vinegar, particularly the trace elements which may be of value in breeding efficiency.

No one seems to have tried this application on people – I wonder what would happen? Reports from research workers would be welcomed.

ARTHRITIS AND RHEUMATISM

More and more farmers are reporting success in the treatment of arthritis and rheumatism even when the cattle have been too lame or stiff to rise or to graze effectively. Two ounces a day of cider vinegar has given cows destined for the stewpot several years of active happy life with useful milk yields. I cannot emphasize too strongly the importance of giving the dosage *regularly*.

A DYSENTRY TYPE SCOUR

Mr I.E.V. of Ellesmere wrote to say that he had a seven-year-old Jersey cow who, for no apparent reason, began a dysentry type scour. The vet was called in, he says, and treated it with an armoury of drugs and drenches. As soon as the treatment ceased the cow immediately became worse again. 'I then decided to try my own herbal medicines. I drenched the cow twice a day with four fluid ounces of cider vinegar, a large tablespoonful of pure honey all in half-a-pint of warm water. After three days the cow had started to chew her cud which was something she had not done for five days on orthodox veterinary treatment.' At the time of writing he said that the cow was still improving steadily and he is now putting cider vinegar in her drinking water.

PIGS
Farrowing Fever
For prevention in suscpetible sows, give them two fluid ounces (50ml) a day for from two to three weeks prior and one to two weeks after farrowing. The piglets are usually more active and the sow does not lose her appetite. If she has farrowing fever then give two ounces (50ml) daily for at least ten days.

Farmer G. Chatham of Kingsbridge found he was constantly having large veterinary bills because of farrowing fever. His losses of pigs and consequent debility were very bad. He used the two fluid ounces (50ml) for two weeks before and one week after treatment and reported a marked improvement in his breeding stock. Since using cider vinegar he had no cases of farrowing fever or similar udder troubles. The young pigs were more lively and less laid on by sows. Since using cider vinegar he was of the opinion that both the quantity and quality of his pigs had greatly improved. He has asked that his experience be shared with other breeders to cut their losses by such a simple but safe treatment.

Scouring
As with calves, bacterial and nutritional scouring is often cured with cider vinegar in the drinking water of pigs.

Farmer K.J.R. of Newport, Isle of Wight had one pig which was scouring so badly it was almost dead. Ten days after the cider vinegar treatment was begun, the pig was back to normal.

Farmer D.F.W. of Chard has twenty-two

breeding sows, some three years old. In the past he has had to have the vet two or three times to each at farrowing time. Now sometimes the vet comes once and sometimes not at all. He is having better litters with nine to twelve reared. His vet's bill is down by two-thirds.

Incidentally, just before farrowing, he gives the sow either a pint (575ml) of stout or one-and-a-half pints (750ml) of rough cider and finds this makes them so docile that they lie down and farrow half asleep!

GOATS

In general, the treatments for goats are about half that for cattle.

Mr J.L.R. of Colchester who has a herd of dairy goats, found cider vinegar particularly effective in the treatment of acetonaemia.

POULTRY

Turkeys and chickens have been reported to show an improved rate of growth when a teaspoonful of cider vinegar is added to each quart (litre) of drinking water.

Mr John Woods of Preston, a poultry keeper on a considerable scale, made a controlled trial on birds in battery cages which had poor shell texture following respiratory infection. He added the cider vinegar at 1 per cent, that is two-and-a-half gallons (10½ litres) per ton of feed. The addition was known to no-one but himself and his mill operative and he frankly said that he had little confidence of any beneficial results. He checked the shell texture at the end of two weeks with no apparent change.

Almost as an afterthought, he checked again at the end of a month and found a most marked improvement. He assessed the number of cracked and porous eggs was reduced by 80 per cent in the treated group.

HORSES AND PONIES

The suggested doses are three fluid ounces a day for small ponies, horses up to fifteen hands four fluid ounces (100ml), and over fifteen hands six ounces (175ml) per day. As many horses are rather conservative in their eating habits it is best to give it with their favourite food. Drenching is not recommended for horses or ponies with cider vinegar or with other fluids for that matter, unless it is done by the veterinary surgeon, as the procedure can lead to respiratory complications.

LOST APPETITE

A ration that is high in concentrates frequently causes horses and ponies to become bored, when they lose interest in their food. The use of cider vinegar on the feed often stimulates the appetite as well as improving the general condition.

DUNG EATING

This rather unpleasant habit is clearly discouraged by the rapid removal of the dung. It could be, however, that it has a nutritional origin because a course of cider vinegar, which is rich in minerals, often cures the condition.

COAT CONDITION

Horses and ponies improve the suppleness and

bloom of their coat when on a course of cider vinegar in a significant number of instances.

POISONING
Because of the effect that cider vinegar has both in improving the appetite and in restoring the intestinal organisms that are so often altered or destroyed either by accidentally-eaten poisons or veterinary treatment with a similar effect — for example, antibiotics often damage the bacteria essential to good health even though they may be necessary for treatment — there will be gradual but helpful assistance from the use of cider vinegar in such circumstances, when used in addition to the usual procedures.

EQUINE INFLUENZA AND COUGH
I have noted only one communication upon this subject, but very interesting.

Lord C. from Dorset writes that he has been feeding cider vinegar to horses for a number of years and although they have mixed freely with sufferers from cough or equine flu, they have so far been immune. Perhaps this is a result of the cider vinegar treatment.

SHEEP
Twin Lamb Disease
This is a toxaemia of pregnancy which usually occurs in ewes in the fourth and fifth months of pregnancy, often when they are carrying two or three lambs. When contracted, it is frequently fatal so prevention is important. The incidence has been said to reduce when two fluid ounces a day of cider

vinegar are sprinkled over the concentrate. Treatment is certainly worth trying by using a drench with quarter-of-a-pint (150ml) of cider vinegar and an equal amount of warm water and then the two ounces (50ml) a day for one or two weeks.

CIDER VINEGAR WORKS WONDERS FOR RACEHORSES

The famous racehorse *Noble Dancer*, who in 1978 won £200,000 ($400,000) in prize money, is a regular user of cider vinegar for health and fitness. More and more trainers are giving their thoroughbred horses cider vinegar and saying that it keeps them in the peak of condition in a quite remarkable way. Indeed several trainers have told me of their experiences with cider vinegar but forbidden me from mentioning their names or their horses because they want to keep this secret weapon to themselves! However, it can be revealed that *Noble Dancer* takes Martlet cider vinegar whereas the famous racehorse trainer, David Morley from near Bury St Edmunds insists that the cider vinegar for all his horses must be made from Aspall organically grown cider vinegar.

USEFUL ADDRESSES

Appleford Limited
Poyle Close
Colnbrook
Slough SL3 0AB

Aspall Cyder House Products
The Cyder House
Aspall Hall
Stowmarket
Suffolk

Martlet Health Food Products
Horam Manor
Horam
Heathfield
Sussex

Whiteways of Whimple Limited
The Orchards
Whimple
Exeter EX5 2QJ

FURTHER READING

The Cider Vinegar and Molasses Recipe Book
  Maurice Hanssen (Thorsons)
Cider Vinegar
  Cyril Scott (Athene)
Country Kitchen Recipes with Cider Vinegar
  Maurice Hanssen (Thorsons)
Cider Apple Vinegar
  H. Hawksey (Science of Life Books)

INDEX

INDEX